A2 in a

50256961 0

Physics

Abbey College, Cambridge

Series Editor: Kevin Byrne

Where to find the information you need

Letts Educational
4 Grosvenor Place, London SW1X 7DL
School enquiries: 01539 564910
Parent & student enquiries: 01539 564913
E-mail: mail@lettsed.co.uk

Website: www.letts-educational.com

Every effort has been made to trace copyright holders and obtain their permission for the use of copyright material. The authors and publishers will gladly receive information enabling them to rectify any error or omission in subsequent editions.

First published 2001
10 9 8 7 6 5

British Library Cataloguing in Publication Data
A CIP record for this book is available from the British Library.

ISBN 978-1-84315-817-2

Cover design by Purple, London

Prepared by *specialist* publishing services, Milton Keynes

Printed in Dubai

Simple Harmonic Motion

25 minutes

Test your knowledge

1 The mass and spring arrangement shown in the diagram oscillates between A and B about equilibrium point O. The mass takes 0.6 s to move from O to B and back to O. Determine:
a) The amplitude of the motion.
b) The period.
c) The frequency.

2 cm

2 cm

A

O

B

2 A mass tied to a string swings back and forth as a pendulum. The amplitude of the motion is 5 cm and the period 1.2 s. Calculate:
a) The maximum acceleration of the mass.
b) The maximum speed of the mass.
c) The speed of the mass at a displacement of 2 cm.
d) The speed of the mass after 0.8 s. ($t = 0$ at centre of oscillation)

3 A body performs SHM with a period T. If timing starts at equilibrium, state, in terms of T, the next three times at which:
a) Acceleration is maximum.
b) Velocity is minimum.

4 If a pendulum has a bob of mass 0.8 kg and length 1.2 m, calculate the period of the motion. ($g = 10 \text{ms}^{-2}$)

5 A child on a swing rises through a height of 0.5 m. Ignoring resistive energy losses, calculate the maximum speed of the child. (The child makes no movement to increase or decrease the swing height.) ($g = 10 \text{ms}^{-2}$)

Answers

1 a) 2cm b) 1.2s c) 0.8Hz 2 a) 1.4ms⁻² b) 0.26ms⁻¹ c) 0.24ms⁻¹ d) 0.13ms⁻¹
3 a) ¼ T, ¾ T, 5⁄4 T b) ½ T, T, 3⁄2 T 4 2.2 s 5 3.2ms⁻¹

If you got them all right, skip to page 6

Simple Harmonic Motion

30 minutes

Improve your knowledge

1 An oscillating or vibrating body is one that performs a repetitive to and fro motion about a fixed point (equilibrium position).

- One cycle of the motion is from one extreme of the motion to the other and back again.

- The amplitude of the oscillation (*r*) is the maximum displacement from the equilibrium position.

- The frequency of the oscillation (*f*) is the number of complete oscillations performed every second.

- The period of the oscillation (*T*) is the time for one complete oscillation.

- Period and frequency are related by:

$$f = \frac{1}{T}$$

Key points from AS in a Week

Basic wave definitions page 48

Work, energy and power;
Principle of conservation of energy   page 30

f is measured in hertz (Hz).

2 Most commonly, oscillating bodies perform simple harmonic motion (SHM). A body performs SHM if it makes a repetitive oscillatory motion about a fixed point where its acceleration is proportional to the displacement from that point and is always directed towards that point.

- This statement is expressed mathematically as:

$$a \propto -x$$
$$a = -\omega^2 x$$

  x = displacement (m)
  a = acceleration (ms^{-2})
  ω^2 = constant of proportionality

  ω is angular velocity (rads^{-1})

  The sign must be minus because the acceleration is always towards a fixed point.

- The velocity of a body performing SHM can be determined at any instant:

$$v = \pm\omega\sqrt{r^2 - x^2}$$

$$\omega = 2\pi f$$
$$\omega = \frac{2\pi}{T}$$

  ± signs indicate that the velocity can be in either direction.

- Therefore:

$$x = r\cos\omega t$$

This equation assumes that timing starts at one extreme of the oscillation.

If timing starts at the centre of the oscillation, $x = r\sin\omega t$.

3 The variation of acceleration, velocity and displacement with time can be represented graphically:

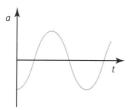 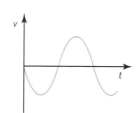 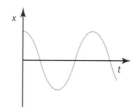

4 Two examples of bodies in SHM are a mass performing vertical oscillations on a spring and a simple pendulum.

- For the spring: $T = 2\pi\sqrt{\dfrac{m}{k}}$

- For the pendulum: $T = 2\pi\sqrt{\dfrac{l}{g}}$

T = period (s)
m = mass (kg)
k = spring constant (Nm^{-1})

l = pivot to centre of mass length (m)

Assumes spring has negligible mass. Otherwise use $m + m_s$, where m_s = effective mass of spring.

5 When a body oscillates there is a continual interchange of kinetic energy and potential energy. For a simple pendulum:

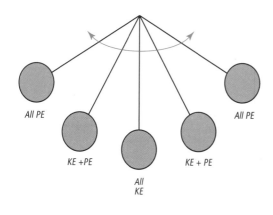

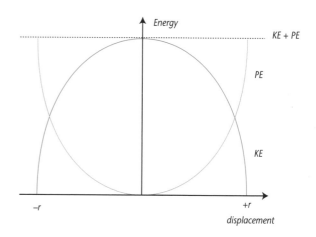

Simple Harmonic Motion

30 minutes

Use your knowledge

1 A body of mass 20 kg moves with simple harmonic motion in a straight line. The period of the motion is 2 s and the maximum force exerted on the particle is 5000 N.
Calculate:
a) The maximum acceleration of the particle.
b) The amplitude of the oscillation.
c) The maximum speed of the particle.
d) The maximum potential energy of the particle.
e) The speed of the particle 1.3 s after leaving the equilibrium position.

$F = ma$

$Max\ PE = max\ KE$

$v = r\omega cos(\omega t)$

2 A mass of 0.5 kg hangs from a vertical spring of spring constant k. The period of the oscillation is T and the amplitude 10 cm.
a) Determine in terms of k:
 i) The maximum velocity.
 ii) The maximum acceleration.
 iii) The velocity at a displacement of 4 cm.
b) The spring is replaced with one of spring constant $2k$ and all other factors remain unchanged. Calculate the following ratios:
 i) Max velocity$_{New\ spring}$/max velocity$_{Old\ spring}$
 ii) Max acceleration$_{New\ spring}$/max acceleration$_{Old\ spring}$

$$T = 2\pi\sqrt{\frac{m}{k}}$$

$$\omega = \frac{2\pi}{T}$$

$$v = r\omega$$

$$v \propto \omega \propto \sqrt{k}$$

$$\therefore 2k \Rightarrow \sqrt{2}v$$

$$a \propto \omega^2 \propto k$$

$$\therefore 2k \Rightarrow 2a$$

Uniform Circular Motion

30 minutes

Test your knowledge

1

a) i) If $r = 7\,cm$, and $s = 21\,cm$ determine θ in radians.
   ii) If θ is increased to π radians, determine s.

b) A particle moves along a circular path at a steady speed. If the line joining the particle to the centre of the circle sweeps out $9\,rad$ in $300\,s$ and the circle has a diameter of $20\,cm$, calculate:
i) The angular speed.
ii) The time for one revolution.
iii) The linear speed of the body.

2

a) An object travelling in a circular path has a changing velocity, even if its _____ is constant. The resulting acceleration acts _____ the _____ of the circle. A body can travel at constant speed in a circle as the _____ force does no _____ on the body.

b) A body of mass $50\,kg$ makes circular motion in a horizontal plane, with a radius of $2\,m$. The period of the rotation is $3\,s$.
i) Calculate the angular speed.
ii) Calculate the linear speed.
iii) Calculate the magnitude of the centripetal force.

3 A stone tied to a string is swung in a horizontal circle at a steady speed. The string has a length of $0.8\,m$ and the angular speed of the rotation is $3.0\,rad\,s^{-1}$. If the maximum tension that the string can withstand before breaking is $14.4\,N$, calculate the maximum mass of stone that can be swung at this speed.

Answers

✓ If you got them all right, skip to page 11

Uniform Circular Motion

Improve your knowledge

 Describing Circular Motion

Key points from
AS in a Week

Resolving vectors
page 10

Basic wave
definitions
page 48

- Angular Displacement

Angles are measured in degrees or radians, where $360° = 2\pi$ radians

To convert from degrees into radians: (radians) = (degrees) $\times \frac{2\pi}{360}$

To convert from radians into degrees: (degrees) = (radians) $\times \frac{360}{2\pi}$

When a body moves along an arc of a circle, of radius r, between points A and B, the angle that the radius sweeps out at the centre is called the angular displacement, θ. By definition: $\theta = \frac{s}{r}$ (θ in radians).

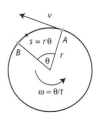

- Angular and linear speed

If the body in the diagram took t seconds to move from A to B, then we define its angular speed (ω) as the angle swept out by the body per second (measured in radians per second).

angular speed
$\omega = \frac{\theta}{t}$
(for constant ω)

The velocity of a body moving in a circular arc will always be changing due to its variation in direction. Because of this we often just refer to the tangential or linear speed (v): this is the speed that the object would have if it left the circular path (e.g. if the string holding it in circular motion broke). This speed depends on the distance between the body and the centre of the circle: as the body covers distance s in time t, its linear speed is $v = s/t = r\theta/t$ *(by $\theta = s/r$)*. From the definition of ω, we can write $v = r\omega$.

- Frequency and time period

Time period (T) of the motion is the time, in seconds, it takes for the body to complete one revolution.
Frequency (f) is the number of revolutions the body will complete in one second. It is measured in units of s^{-1}, also called Hz (hertz).

$f = \frac{1}{T}$

So angular velocity is given by $\omega = 2\pi f$.

Uniform Circular Motion

2 Explaining circular motion

- An object following a circular path is not moving in a straight line! Therefore, even if the object has a constant linear speed (v), it has a changing velocity, as velocity is a vector and the object is changing direction.

- As acceleration is the rate of change of velocity, this gives rise to an acceleration in the direction of the change of velocity. Because this acts towards the centre of the circle, it is termed the centripetal (centre-seeking) acceleration. It has magnitude:

$$a = v^2/r = r\omega^2$$

- By Newton's Second Law, an accelerating body must have a resultant force acting on it. We call the resultant force acting in towards the centre of the circle the centripetal force (F_c).

$$F_c = ma = mv^2/r = mr\omega^2$$

This is not a new type of force, but simply the name we give to the unbalanced force acting towards the centre of the circle for any object moving in a circular path.

- When a body moves in a circle at constant speed and height (horizontal circle) the centripetal force acting on the body is towards the centre of the circle – the body does not move in this direction. Therefore, as work done is defined as the product of force and distance moved in the direction of the force, no work is done by the body.

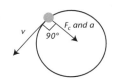

3 Examples of uniform circular motion

- Gravity (e.g. satellites or planets)

In this case the only force acting on the satellite (or planet) is its weight (i.e. gravitational attraction towards the body it orbits). This is given by Newton's Law of Gravitation (see chapter on Gravitation): Weight = GMm/r^2 and provides the centripetal force.

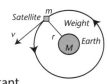

Weight = Centripetal force
$GMm/r^2 = mv^2/r$
$\quad v = \sqrt{(GM/r)}$

or $GMm/r^2 = mr\omega^2$
$\quad T^2 = (4\pi^2/GM)\ r^3$ where $\omega = 2\pi f = 2\pi/T$

G	universal gravitational constant
M	mass of the earth
m	mass of the satellite
r	distance from the centre of the body to the satellite

When the only force acting on an object is gravitational, the object is in freefall. In such cases (e.g. astronauts in space) people experience apparent weightlessness, as they accelerate at the same rate as the object they are in and there is no contact (normal reaction) force between them and the object.

Uniform Circular Motion

- 'Conical pendulum' and banked track or aircraft questions

The conical pendulum consists of an object on a piece of string, hanging from a hook. The object moves in a horizontal circular path.

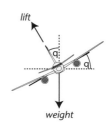

In this case the unbalanced force is the horizontal component of the tension in the string ($T\cos\theta$). This provides the centripetal force:

Resolving horizontally: $T\cos\theta = mv^2/r$

   where r is the radius of the horizontal circle.

We find the tension in the string by resolving vertically, where the weight (mg) is balanced by the vertical component of the tension in the string ($T\sin\theta$):

Resolving vertically: $T\sin\theta = mg$

The angle the string makes with the vertical (θ) is usually found from trigonometry: if the object is a height h below the hook, $\theta = \tan^{-1}(h/r)$

In similar questions, an aircraft in horizontal flight turns in a circle of radius r by banking at $\theta°$ while travelling at a constant speed v.

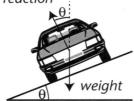

Alternatively, a question may ask about a car travelling in a circle of radius r at a constant speed (v) and height around a track banked at $\theta°$. You can answer all these questions using a similar method.

- Magnetism

Charged particles injected at right angles into a magnetic field will describe uniform circular motion (see Synoptic chapter).

Uniform Circular Motion

35 minutes

Use your knowledge

1 a) Explain why a body moving with uniform speed in a circular path experiences an acceleration.

b) Write an equation to define this force, defining all terms used.

c) The gravitational force acting on a satellite of mass m, a distance r away from the centre of the Earth, of mass M, is given by $F = GMm/r^2$, where G is the universal gravitational constant. ($g = 9.81\,\text{ms}^{-2}$)

   i) Write an equation relating the centripetal force to the gravitational force for the satellite.

   ii) Solve this to find how fast a satellite must travel to orbit the Earth at a height of two Earth's radii. ($r_E = 6.4 \times 10^6\,\text{m}$)

$GM/r_E = gr_E$

2 a) Calculate the angular speed of the man in the diagram.

b) Calculate his linear speed.

c) Calculate his acceleration due to the Earth's rotation.

d) How does the acceleration for a geostationary satellite, one Earth radius above the surface of the Earth, compare to your answer for part c)?

1 rotation = 24 hours

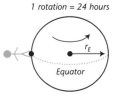

Equator

$r_E = 6.4 \times 10^6\,m$

3 A car travels around a circular track at a steady speed of $15\,\text{ms}^{-1}$. The mass of the car is 950 kg and the distance from the centre of the track to the centre of the circle is 20 m.

a) In which direction does the resultant force on the car always act?

b) Calculate the size of this force.

c) What provides this force?

d) Calculate the corresponding acceleration.

4 A child ties a 500 g mass to a 1 m length of string and swings it in a horizontal circle as shown. The string makes an angle of 60° to the horizontal.

a) Calculate ($g = 10\text{ms}^{-2}$):

   i) The tension in the string.

   ii) The centripetal force.

   iii) The period of the motion.

   iv) The linear speed.

b) Why can't the string be horizontal?

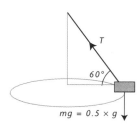

T

$60°$

$mg = 0.5 \times g$

Gravitation

Test your knowledge

1 All bodies are surrounded by a region called a _____ field.
Within this field all other bodies will experience an _____ force.

2 a) Calculate the force between the Earth and a 20 kg mass, where the separation of their centres is 20 000 km. ($G = 6.7 \times 10^{-11}\,Nm^2kg^{-2}$, $m_{Earth} = 6.0 \times 10^{24}\,kg$)

b) If the force acting between two identical masses is F, then calculate, in terms of F, the force acting when their separation is halved and each mass is doubled.

3 Calculate the magnitude of the gravitational field strength at A.

$r = 2 \times 10^6\,m$

$\longrightarrow A$ ($G = 6.7 \times 10^{-11}\,Nm^2kg^{-2}$)

$m = 1 \times 10^4\,kg$

4 a) What is the defined value of gravitational potential at infinity?

b) What do all other values, at all the other locations, have in common?

5 a) Calculate the gravitational potential at point A in Question 3.

b) Calculate the potential energy that a $4 \times 10^3\,kg$ mass would have at point A in Question 3.

6 Calculate the work done moving a 20 kg body from the surface of the Earth to a point 800 km from the surface of the Earth.
($G = 6.7 \times 10^{-11}\,Nm^2kg^{-2}$, $m_{Earth} = 6.0 \times 10^{24}\,kg$, $r_{Earth} = 6.4 \times 10^6\,m$).

7 If the dotted lines are equipotentials, how do you know that the solid line is not a correct representation of the corresponding field line?

Answers

✔ **If you got them all right, skip to page 15**

Gravitation

Improve your knowledge

1 A gravitational field is a region within which a mass will experience a force.

Any two bodies with mass will exert attractive forces upon each other, as long as each mass is within the gravitational field of the other.

Key points from
AS in a Week

Addition of vectors
pages 8–9

2 Newton's Law of Gravitation states the attractive force between two bodies is:

- Proportional to the product of their masses.

- Inversely proportional to the square of the separation of their centres.

$$F \propto \frac{mM}{r^2}$$

$$F = \frac{GmM}{r^2}$$

G = universal gravitational constant

$$= 6.7 \times 10^{-11}\,\text{Nm}^2\text{kg}^{-2}$$

3 Gravitational field strength at a given point is defined as the force exerted per unit mass (1 kg) at that point in the field:

where g = gravitational field strength (Nkg^{-1} or ms^{-2}).

$$g = \frac{F}{m}$$

A field due to a spherical body has a gravitational field strength at a given point determined by substituting $m = 1\,\text{kg}$ into the force equation.

1 kg

- At point A: $g = \frac{GM}{r^2}$

- The resultant gravitational field strength due to more than one body is determined by vectorially adding the individual field strengths.

4 The gravitational potential (V) at a given point in a field is defined as the work done in bringing a unit mass (1 kg) from infinity to that point in the field.

- The potential (and hence potential energy of all bodies) at infinity is defined to be zero. Work has to be done on a mass to move it towards infinity, yet at infinity it would have zero potential energy. All points other than infinity must therefore, have negative potentials.

- At point A: $W = \frac{-GM}{r}$

$$PE = \frac{-GMm}{r}$$

Gravitation

The total potential due to more than one body at a given point in a field is determined by adding the individual potentials as scalars.

5 The potential energy a body possesses at a given point in a field is determined by multiplying the magnitude of the mass by the value of the field's gravitational potential.

- At point A: $PE = \dfrac{-GMm}{r}$

6 The work done in moving a body between two given points in a field is determined by subtracting the body's initial potential energy from its final potential energy.

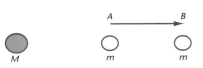

- If the body is moved from A to B:

    Work done $= mV_B - mV_A = m(V_B - V_A)$

7 Gravitational field lines indicate the strength and direction of the field. The strength of the field is indicated by the closeness of the lines.

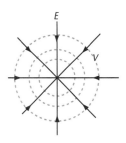

- For a spherical mass such as a planet the field lines are always directed towards the body, and arranged radially.

- Lines joining points of the same potential are known as equipotential lines.

- Field lines and equipotentials are always perpendicular to each other.

Gravitation

35 minutes

Use your knowledge

1 Calculate the gravitational potential at the surface of the Earth.
($G = 6.7 \times 10^{-11}\,Nm^2kg^{-2}$, $m_{Earth} = 6.0 \times 10^{24}\,kg$, $r_{Earth} = 6.4 \times 10^6\,m$)

2 Calculate the work done moving a mass of 1000 kg along the paths indicated on the diagram below:
a) Path I.
b) Path II.
c) Path III.

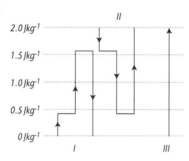

Work done = final PE − initial PE. The path followed is irrelevant. If the change in potential is zero then the work done is zero.

3

The xs cancel out. The fields are in opposite directions, so subtract.

a) Calculate the gravitational field strength at A in terms of G.
b) Calculate, in terms of G, the potential energy of a body of mass $50/\sqrt{x}$ at A.

4 If a human's height is in inverse proportion to the gravitational field strength of her planet, how tall would a 1.8 m human be if she were born on a planet with half the Earth's radius and twice its mass?

If $g_{planet}/g_{Earth} = K$ then height on planet = height on Earth $\times$ 1/K

Electrostatics

Test your knowledge

1 A _____ body will have a force exerted upon it if it is placed in an _____ field.

2 Calculate the magnitude of the force between the charged particles.

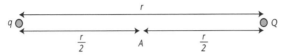

$q = 2.4 \times 10^{-17}$ C
$Q = 4.8 \times 10^{-17}$ C
$r = 2.0 \times 10^{-11}$ m
$\varepsilon_0 = 8.85 \times 10^{-12}$ Fm^{-1}

3 What is the magnitude and the direction of the electric field strength at point *A* in the above example?

4 a) The definition of electrical potential involves:
   i)   Which type of charge?
   ii) Which energy term?
   iii) A reference point at zero potential by definition. Where is it?
   b) What is the value of the electrical potential at point *A* in Question 2?

5 If the charges *Q* and *q* have a potential energy of 5.5×10^{-8} J, determine *r*.

$q = 4.5 \times 10^{-9}$ C
$Q = 8.2 \times 10^{-9}$ C
$\varepsilon_0 = 8.85 \times 10^{-12}$ Fm^{-}

6 How much work is done in moving *q* from *A* to *B* in the above example?

7 a) At which point is the field strength the greatest?
   b) What is the geometrical relationship between field lines and equipotentials?

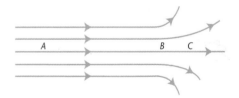

Answers

✔ **If you got them all right, skip to page 19**

Electrostatics

Improve your knowledge

1 An electric field is a region within which a charged body will experience a force.

The direction of the field is the direction in which a small positive charge would be forced to move if positioned within the field.

Key points from AS in a Week

Addition of vectors pages 8–9

2 Two charged particles will exert equal and opposite forces upon each other, since each charge is within the electric field of the other.

The magnitude of the force is determined by Coulomb's Law: $F = \dfrac{1}{4\pi\varepsilon_0} \dfrac{Qq}{r^2}$

ε_0 = permittivity of free space = 8.85×10^{-12} Fm^{-1}

3 Electric field strength at a given point is defined as the force exerted per unit positive (+1C) charge at that point in the field.

where $E = \dfrac{F}{q}$

i.e. E = electric field strength (NC^{-1})

A field due to a point charge has an electric field strength, at a given position, determined by:

at point A: $\qquad$ $E = \dfrac{1}{4\pi\varepsilon_0} \dfrac{Q}{r^2}$

The resultant electric field strength due to more than one point charge is determined by vectorially adding the individual field strengths.

4 The electrical potential at a given point in a field is defined as:

The work done in bringing a unit positive charge from infinity to that point in the field.

- At point A: $\quad V = \dfrac{Q}{4\pi\varepsilon_0 r}$

- The total potential at a given point in a field due to more than one point charge is determined by adding the individual potentials as scalars.

Electrostatics

5 The potential energy that a charge possesses at a given point in the field is determined by multiplying the magnitude of the charge by the value of the field's electrical potential.

Q ●←————→ A
r

For q at A: $PE = qV$

$$PE = \frac{qQ}{4\pi\varepsilon_0 r}$$

6 The work done in moving a charge between two given points in a field is determined by subtracting the charge's initial potential energy from its final potential energy.

- If the charged particle is moved from A to B.
  Work done $= qV_B - qV_A = q(V_B - V_A)$

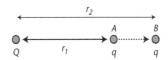

7 Field lines indicate the strength and direction of electric fields.

- The strength of the field is indicated by how close together the lines are.

- Lines joining points of the same potential are known as equipotential lines.

- Field lines and equipotentials are always perpendicular to each other.

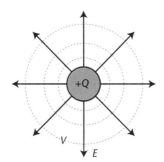

Positively-charged body

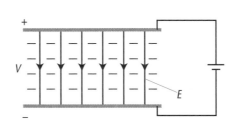

Electrostatics

Use your knowledge

1

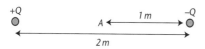

+Q   A ←   1 m   →   −Q

2 m

$\varepsilon_0 = 8.85 \times 10^{-12}\,Fm^{-1}$

$Q = 5.0 \times 10^{-3}\,C$

a) Calculate the forces acting on the particles and indicate the direction in which they act.

b) Determine the new force if the particle separation triples.

c) Calculate the resultant force that would act upon a third particle with a charge 2Q placed at A.

a) Use Coulomb's Law

b) $F \propto 1/r^2$

c) Calculate the force exerted by each charge independently. Find the resultant.

2

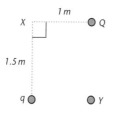

X ⋯⋯ 1 m ⋯⋯ ● Q

1.5 m

q ●   ● Y

$\varepsilon_0 = 8.85 \times 10^{-12}\,Fm^{-1}$

$Q = 8.0 \times 10^{-5}\,C$

$q = 12 \times 10^{-5}\,C$

a) Calculate the magnitude of the electric field strength at X.

b) Calculate the value of the potential at X.

c) How much work is done when a 2 μC charge is moved from X to Y?

Find field strengths due to q and Q and add as vectors.

Potentials add as scalars.

Work done = final PE − initial PE

3

a) Calculate the values of work done if a 2 μC particle is moved along each path.
  i) Path A.
  ii) Path B.
  iii) Path C.

b) Add three field lines to the diagram.

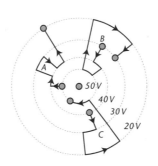

Work done = charge × (final potential − initial potential)

20 minutes

Test your knowledge

 1 In which direction is the current in the circuit?

Explain your answer.

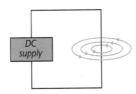

 2 a) State the factors that influence the magnitude of the magnetic flux density along the axis of an air-cored long solenoid.

b) A current causes a magnetic flux density, B, along the axis of a solenoid. Determine the magnetic flux density, in terms of B, for a solenoid with the same current flowing through it which has the same number of turns, but is twice as long with half the diameter.

 3 The wire conductor in the diagram is perpendicular to a field of magnetic flux density 0.25 T. The current is 2 A.

a) Calculate the magnitude of the force on the wire.

b) Determine the direction in which the wire would move.

c) The two wires in the diagram would _____ each other, since each wire is in the _____ of the other. The magnitude of this force is _____ N. ($\mu_0 = 4\pi \times 10^{-7}\,Hm^{-1}$)

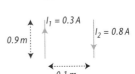

 4 A Hall probe is used to measure magnetic flux density.

a) Briefly describe how the Hall probe is used to measure field strength.

b) Describe how the field direction is determined.

 If you got them all right, skip to page 25

Magnetism

30 minutes

Improve your knowledge

1 Whenever charged particles move, they create a magnetic field around them. Therefore, sources of magnetic fields are:

- Moving charges in space
- Permanent Magnets – due to electron motion in atoms
- Current-carrying conductors (e.g. wires)

Key points from AS in a Week	
Current	page 34
Turning forces	page 25

- *straight wire* (concentric circular field lines)
  To establish the direction of the field lines: grip the wire in your right hand with your thumb pointing in the direction of the current. The direction of the field lines is that in which your fingers wrap around the wire.

- *solenoid*
  Grip the solenoid in your right hand with your fingers wrapped around the coil in the direction of the current. Your thumb will point to the north pole (field N to S).

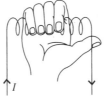

North

2 Magnetic flux density (*B*) indicates the strength and direction of a magnetic field and so is more easily thought of as the field strength. It is a vector quantity with the units tesla (T).

long straight wire $B = \dfrac{\mu_0 I}{2\pi r}$

r = perpendicular distance to wire

along the axis of a long solenoid $B = \dfrac{\mu_0 N I}{L}$

    N = number of turns
    L = length of solenoid
    I = current in wire

Permeability, $\mu = \mu_0 \mu_r$
μ_0 = permeability of free space
  $(4\pi \times 10^{-7}\ \text{Hm}^{-1})$
μ_r = relative permeability
μ_r is a measure of how much a material enhances the magnetic field strength

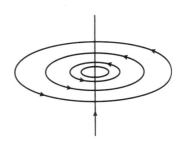

Material	μ_r
Air	1
Iron	10^3

Magnetism

Field lines show field strength, in both size (the closer the lines, the stronger the field) and direction (see point 1). Field lines go from magnetic north to south.

Fields are combined at a point by adding the field strengths vectorally. See below for an example using two parallel wires carrying equal currents.

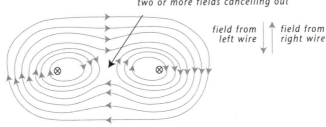

Null or neutral point: *Zero total field strength due to two or more fields cancelling out*

Magnetism requires 3D, so we show lines coming OUT of the pages as ⊙, and those going IN to the page as ⊗

field from left wire | field from right wire

 If a current-carrying conductor is placed in a magnetic field, it will experience a force.

- The size of the force is given by:

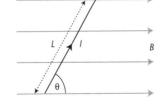

$F = BIL\sin\theta$ B = field strength
I = wire current
L = length of wire in the field
θ = angle between I and B

This is greatest when the conductor is perpendicular to the field lines and zero when it is parallel with the field lines.

- The direction of the force is determined using Fleming's left hand rule.

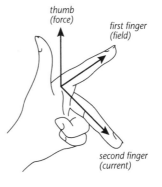

thumb (force)

first finger (field)

second finger (current)

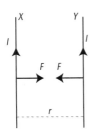

- If two parallel wires carry a current, they will exert a force upon each other, as each wire is in the field of the other. (NB By Newton's Third Law these forces are equal and opposite.)

Currents in the same direction attract.

Currents in opposite directions repel.

The force felt by wire Y due to the magnetic flux density of wire X is given by:

$$F_Y = B_X I_Y L_Y = \frac{\mu_0 I_X I_Y L_Y}{2\pi r} \quad \text{(using } F = BIL \text{ and } \frac{\mu_0 I}{2\pi r} \text{)}$$

end view of wires carrying current into diagram

field line due to wire Y

field line due to wire X

- **The ampere** is defined as the steady current which, when flowing in each of two infinitely long straight parallel conductors with negligible cross-sectional area placed 1 metre apart in a vacuum, causes each conductor to experience a force of 2×10^{-7} N per metre of each other's length.

- **The motor effect.**

A current-carrying coil in a magnetic field will experience a couple.

The current in the left-hand side of the coil is in the opposite direction to that in the right, so the forces on each side will be equal and opposite, resulting in a torque.

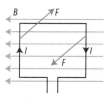

Torque = $NIAB$

N = number of turns
I = current in wire
A = area of coil
B = field strength

B = field strength (T)
q = charge (C)
v = velocity (ms^{-1})
θ = angle between v and B

Motion of charged particles. If a charge is moving in a magnetic field, it is subject to a force.

- **Size of the force** $\quad F = Bqv\sin\theta$

- **Direction of the force** is at right angles to the field and velocity, as given by Fleming's LHR.
  Remember the conventional current is the direction of flow for positive charge and so the flow of negatively charged particles is in the opposite direction. Charged particles move in circular paths in a perpendicular magnetic field (see Synoptic chapter).

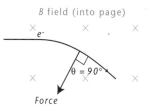

The Hall probe is used to measure magnetic fields.

- It consists of a thin rectangular slice of semiconductor material, which develops a voltage (the Hall voltage) across its width when a current is passed through the length of the slice while it is at right angles to a steady magnetic field.

- The Hall voltage ($\sim 10^{-6}$V) is directly proportional to the magnetic flux density of the field. It is recorded by a calibrated high resistance voltmeter (digital voltmeter or CRO).

- The field direction is at right angles (90°) to the probe when the maximum voltage is recorded, which is itself proportional to the field strength. (See Synoptic chapter for more).

$$V_H = Bvd$$

V_H = Hall voltage (V)
B = field strength (T)
v = mean drift velocity of charge carriers (ms^{-1})
d = width of slice (m)

Magnetism

Use your knowledge

1 The attractive force exerted on each of these parallel wires is found to be 4×10^{-7} N.
($\mu_0 = 4\pi \times 10^{-7}$ Hm^{-1})

a) Determine the direction of I.
b) Calculate the magnitude of I.

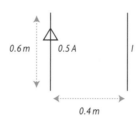

2 X and Y are magnets with opposite poles facing each other. The magnetic flux density in the gap is B. The length of the wire in the field is 30 cm, arranged perpendicularly to the field. The wire between the poles has an effective mass of 9 g and is in equilibrium. ($g = 10$ ms^{-2})

a) Determine the magnetic polarity of X and Y.
b) Calculate the magnitude of B.

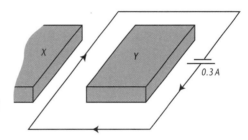

Use Fleming's left-hand rule.

Rearrange $F = BIL$

F must equal the weight of the wire.

3 The 50-turn coil in the diagram below will rotate 0.5° for each 0.025 Nm of torque exerted upon it. The field is radial (always perpendicular to the coil). If the current in the coil is 0.2 A and the magnetic flux density is 0.5 T, then:

a) Determine in which direction the coil rotates.
b) Calculate the angle through which the coil rotates.

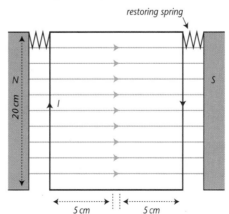

Use Fleming's left-hand rule either side of the coil.

Divide torque by 0.025 to determine the number of 0.5° rotations.

Magnetic Induction

Test your knowledge

1 A 5-turn coil of diameter 3 cm is positioned in a magnetic field ($B = 2 \times 10^{-6}$ T). Calculate its flux linkage when the coil is:
a) Perpendicular to the field.
b) Parallel to the field.
c) Positioned with its normal at 25° to the field.

2 An EMF is induced when there is a change in the _____ through a conductor. This is described by _____ Law. In addition, the induced EMF acts to _____ the change that created it. This is _____ Law and is a form of _____ conservation.

3 a) The horizontal metal rod moves through the vertical magnetic field at 3 ms^{-1}. 0.8 m of the conductor is in the field, which has a magnetic flux density of 0.7 T.
   i) Calculate the EMF induced across the ends of the rod.
   ii) In which direction (looking from above) would the current flow in the circuit?

b) A square coil with 20 turns of side 5 cm is removed from a field of 2×10^{-4} T in 0.4 s.
   i) Determine the EMF induced in the coil.
   ii) Explain which pole would be induced to the left-hand side of the coil.

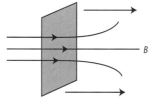

4 One of a pair of coils has a current that increases at 0.5 A each second, and the other is electrically isolated. Calculate the EMF induced in the isolated coil. ($M = 0.2$ H)

Answers

1 a) 7.1×10^{-9}Wb b) 0 c) 6×10^{-9}Wb
2 flux/Faraday's/oppose/Lenz's/energy   3 a)i) 1.7V ii) Anti-clockwise
b)i) 2.5×10^{-5}V ii) South pole, because the field lines indicate that the coil is being moved away from a north pole (Lenz's Law).   4 0.1V

 If you got them all right, skip to page 30

Magnetic Induction

30 minutes

Improve your knowledge

 1

Magnetic Flux (ϕ) can be thought of as the total number of flux (or field) lines passing (perpendicularly) through an area A (e.g. of a coil). The unit is the weber (Wb). The flux through an area A is given by:

$$\phi = B^{\perp}A = BA\cos\theta$$

$B^{\perp}$ = the component of B perpendicular to the area A
θ = the angle between B and the normal of the area

> **Key points from AS in a Week**
> Current electricity
> page 34

Magnetic flux density (B) is equivalent to field strength (see 'Magnetism' chapter). We can think of the strength of a field as the number of field lines passing through a unit area perpendicular to the field.

Magnetic flux linkage (Φ) is defined as the product of the flux, ϕ, and the total number of turns of coil through which it passes, N.

> Flux linkage = $N\phi = BAN\cos\theta$

Magnetic flux linkage has the same unit as flux, the weber (Wb). It can be thought of as the 'amount' of magnetic flux contained in a volume (e.g. a solenoid).

 2

When the flux through a conductor changes, an EMF is induced. The more rapid the change in flux linkage, the greater the induced EMF. Two laws describe this:

- **Faraday's Law:** An EMF is induced in direct proportion to the rate of change of flux linkage for the circuit.

- **Lenz's Law:** The direction of the induced EMF acts to oppose the change creating it. It is a form of energy conservation.

These laws are encapsulated by the following equation:

Induced EMF = – rate of change of flux linkage

$$E = -\frac{\text{final flux linkage} - \text{initial flux linkage}}{\text{time for change}} = -N\frac{d\phi}{dt}$$

Minus sign indicates that the induced EMF opposes the change in flux linkage.

Magnetic Induction

There are two main ways in which an EMF can be induced:

1) A conductor moves through a field, 'cutting' flux lines (e.g. a wire moving through a steady field). See 3) below.

2) A magnetic field moves or changes strength in the presence of a stationary conductor. (e.g. a stationary coil in an alternating magnetic field). See 4) below.

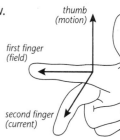

thumb (motion)

first finger (field)

second finger (current)

3 Induction method (1): A conductor moves through a field, 'cutting' flux lines.

If a straight metallic conductor (wire) is moved through a magnetic field then each electron in the metal has a force exerted on it by the field. The free electrons in the metal will move along the wire inducing an EMF (E). If the wire is connected to a complete circuit a current will flow.

- The magnitude of the induced EMF is given by:
  $E = Blv$

- The direction of the induced current is given by Fleming's right hand rule.

B = magnetic flux density perpendicular to wire

l = length of conductor in field

v = speed that conductor is moved through the field

This effect is observed across aircraft wings as the aircraft cuts the Earth's magnetic field.

- The generator, or dynamo, operates in reverse to the motor: kinetic energy is transferred into electrical energy through the creation of an induced EMF from the motion of a coil in a magnetic field. As the coil rotates, the area perpendicular to the flux changes. This creates a rate of change of flux and induces an EMF which varies with time as shown, creating an alternating voltage.

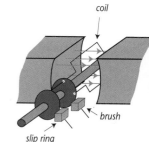

coil

brush

slip ring

$E = BAN\omega\sin(\omega t)$
E = induced EMF
B = magnetic flux density
A = area enclosed by coil
N = number of coils
ω = angular speed ($\omega = 2\pi f$)

EMF

$BAn\omega$

1 cycle

0

Time

$BAn\omega$

If the frequency is increased then two effects are seen:

1) The rate at which the coil cuts flux increases, so the maximum induced EMF increases.

2) As the coil takes less time to complete a revolution, the frequency of the induced voltage also increases.

 Induction method (2): A magnetic field moves or changes strength in the presence of a stationary conductor.

Mutual Inductance. If two coils are close together, a current flow in one will create a flux in the other. If the current in the first coil changes, this will cause a change in the flux in the second coil and hence induce an EMF. The converse of this is true: a current flowing in the second coil would induce and EMF in the first. This is known as mutual inductance. The magnitude of the induced EMF is given by:

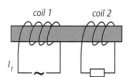

$$E_2 = -M\frac{dI_1}{dt}$$

E_2 = induced EMF in coil 2 (V), M = mutual inductance (H)
dI_1 = change in current, dt = time for change
dI/dt = rate of change of current in first coil

This is the principle upon which the transformer is based. Transformers are used in power stations and sub-stations to step up or step down the voltage in the power supply, in order to avoid large energy losses when transporting electricity over the National Grid.

- Turns ratio = voltage ratio: $N_1/N_2 = V_1/V_2$

- We assume transformers are 100% efficient, i.e.
  Power In = Power Out: $I_1V_1 = I_2V_2$

Eddy currents. Any piece of metal can have an EMF induced in it. This can cause currents to flow in it, even if it is not connected to a circuit. We call these eddy currents: induced currents that flow around low resistance pathways in a conductor when subjected to a varying magnetic field. These are a source of energy dissipation, which can be useful or problematic.

• Useful example: Emergency brakes. A strong magnet is brought near the metal wheel drum, inducing eddy currents. These produce magnetic fields that oppose the motion that produced them (Lenz's Law) and so rapidly slow the vehicle down. In order to come to a halt, conventional brakes are required.

• Problematic example: Iron cores are used in transformers to channel the magnetic field from the primary coil to the secondary. The alternating magnetic field in the iron (a metal) induces eddy currents that dissipate energy through heating effects. In order to minimise this, layers of insulation are inserted in to the core to reduce low-resistance pathways. This is termed a 'laminated' core.

30 minutes

Use your knowledge

1 Two identical coils are mounted close together with a common axis. Coil *A* has a varying current, which induces a current in coil *B*. The top graph plots the current magnitude in coil *A* against time. Sketch a corresponding current time graph for coil *B*. Label significant times and currents.
($M = 4 \times 10^{-4}$ H, $R_B = 1$ kΩ)

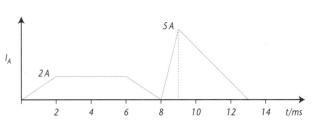

If coil A current is constant, induced current is zero.

2 An aeroplane of wing span 16 m flies from the Equator towards the North Pole. The wings are perpendicular to the vertical component of the Earth's magnetic field ($B = 4 \times 10^{-5}$ T). At maximum speed, an EMF of 96 mV is induced across the wing tips. Calculate the maximum speed of the aeroplane.

Rearrange:
$E = Blv$

3 A 2000-turn coil of diameter 0.02 m is rotated from position *X* to position *Y* in 0.4 s. If the magnetic flux density is 2 T then calculate:

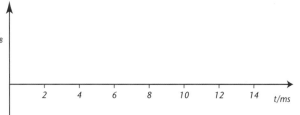

a) Flux linkage in position *X*.
b) Flux linkage in position *Y*.
c) The EMF induced as the coil is moved from *X* to *Y*.

$\phi = BA$

Flux linkage = Nϕ

If CSA is parallel to field flux = zero

$E = \dfrac{-d(N\phi)}{dt}$

Test your knowledge

1 a) Calculate the RMS voltage of an AC supply of peak value 100 V.

   b) If the supply has a frequency of 50 Hz determine the magnitude of the voltage 0.008 s following a zero voltage.

2 If the RMS current in a circuit is 1.5 A provided by a 20 V peak supply, determine the impedance of the circuit.

3 Calculate the inductive reactance of a 0.8 H inductor connected to a 100 Hz AC supply.

4 The capacitive reactance of a capacitor connected to an AC supply is measured to be X_c. Determine, in terms of X_c, the new capacitive reactance if the capacitance and supply frequency are doubled.

5 Determine the total impedance for a 100 Ω resistor, a 2 H inductor, and a 50 μF capacitor connected in series with a 30 Hz AC supply.

6 Determine the power dissipated in the circuit described above, if connected to a 50 V RMS AC supply.

7 An AC supply is connected to the imput terminals of an oscilloscope and the following trace is observed.
Calculate the:
a) peak voltage
b) supply frequency.

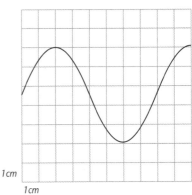

1cm

1cm

Y-Gain = 3 V per cm
Time base = 100 ms per cm

8 _____ is the conversion of _____ current to direct _____ . _____ wave rectification is achieved by placing a diode in _____ with the supply, and _____ wave _____ by using a _____ rectifier circuit.

AC Theory

Improve your knowledge

Key points from
AS in a Week
Resistance page 34

1 The voltage of an AC power supply has a polarity that repetitively reverses in a sinusoidal manner.

- The variation of voltage with time is represented by:

$$V = V_p \sin \omega t$$

where

$$\omega = 2\pi f$$

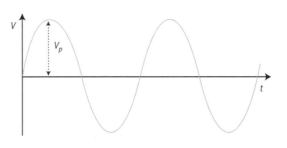

Calculator in rad mode

- When determining the effects of AC voltages, root mean square (RMS) values are often used:

$$V_{RMS} = \frac{V_p}{\sqrt{2}} \qquad I_{RMS} = \frac{I_p}{\sqrt{2}}$$

V_p = peak voltage
ω = angular frequency
t = time
f = frequency of supply

2 The total resistance of a circuit to AC is called impedance (Z). The unit of impedance is the ohm (Ω).

$$Z = \frac{V_{RMS}}{I_{RMS}}$$

Resistors, capacitors and inductors can contribute to the total impedance.

If the circuit contains only resistors, Z = R

3 If an AC supply is connected across an inductor (coil), a back-EMF is induced, hindering the current. This resistance to AC is called inductive reactance X_L.

- The greater the frequency, the greater the inductive reactance:

$$X_L = \omega L = 2\pi f L$$

where L = inductance (H).

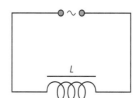

AC Theory

 When an AC supply is connected across a capacitor, the resistance to the current is greater the smaller the capacitance and frequency. The resistance due to a capacitor is known as capacitive reactance X_C.

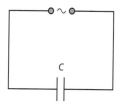

$$X_C = \frac{1}{\omega C} = \frac{1}{2\pi f C}$$

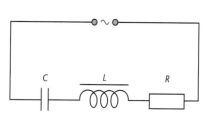

A circuit containing a series arrangement of a capacitor, an inductor and a resistor is known as an LCR circuit.

- The total reactance (impedance) is given by:

$$Z^2 = R^2 + \left(\omega L - \frac{1}{\omega C}\right)^2$$

- If $\omega L = \dfrac{1}{\omega C}$ the current in the circuit is at a maximum,

  resonance is said to occur at maximum current.

 Alternating current causes heating of resistive components only. This means power is dissipated, where

$$P = I_{RMS}{}^2 R = \frac{I^2 R}{2}$$

or

$$\text{average power} = \frac{1}{2} I^2 R$$

AC Theory

A cathode ray oscilloscope (CRO) can be used to measure alternating current parameters.

The Y-gain gives the number of volts per vertical centimetre.

The time base gives the number of milliseconds per horizontal centimetre.

In this example;
Y-gain = $1\,Vcm^{-1}$, time base = $10\,mscm^{-1}$
Peak-to-trough height = 6 cm,
Peak-to-peak voltage = Y-gain × height = $1 \times 6 = 6V$
Peak voltage = Peak-to-peak voltage/2 = 6/3 = 2V
Horizontal = 3 squares
AC period = T = length of one wave × Time Base = $3 \times 10 = 30\,ms$

Frequency = 1/T = $1/30 \times 10^{-3}$ = 33Hz

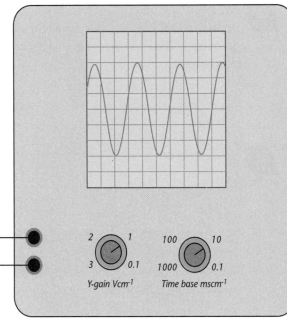

2   1
3   0.1
Y-gain Vcm⁻¹

100   10
1000   0.1
Time base mscm⁻¹

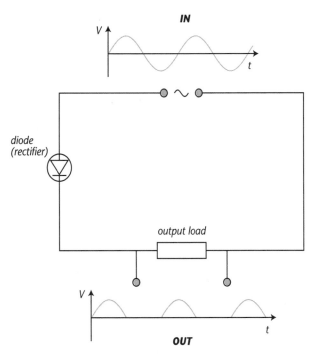

IN

diode (rectifier)

output load

V

t

OUT

An AC voltage can be converted to a DC voltage by rectification.

Half wave rectification produces a current which is direct in that it only flows in one direction, but its magnitude varies periodically.

The diode only conducts in one direction; therefore one half of the potential difference variation cycle is removed.

AC Theory

To achieve full wave rectification (no gaps in the waveform) a bridge rectifier circuit is used.

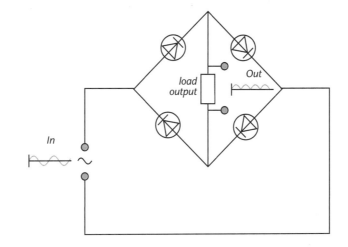

Smoothing converts the varying magnitude output of the rectifier circuits to one that is closer to a constant value DC supply. This is achieved by connecting a capacitor in parallel with the rectifier output.

When the potential difference across the output load is increasing (i.e. at X) the capacitor is charging. When the potential difference across the output load falls, the capacitor discharges through the output load, i.e. fills the gaps in the waveform. Both half wave and full wave rectified signals can be smoothed in this manner.

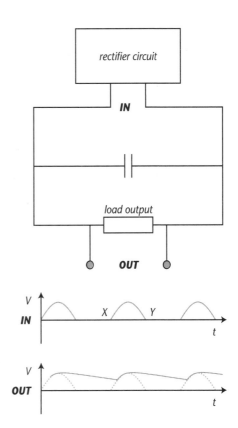

AC Theory

Use your knowledge

1 The voltage of an AC supply varies as shown in the diagram.

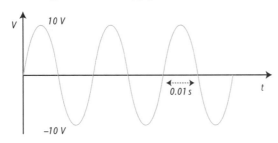

a) Determine the frequency of the supply.
b) Calculate the angular frequency of the supply.
c) State the peak voltage value.
d) How long after $t = 0$ is the voltage first equal to 2.5 V?

$T = 0.02s$

$\omega = 2\pi f$

$V = V_p \sin \omega t$

$\omega t = \sin^{-1}(V/V_p)$

2

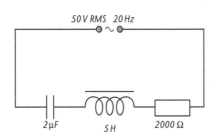

50 V RMS 20 Hz

2 µF   5 H   2000 Ω

a) Calculate the impedance of the circuit.
b) Determine I_{RMS}.
c) At which supply frequency value would the current have its maximum possible value?
d) Determine the RMS value of this maximum current.
e) If the power dissipated at the original frequency is P and the power at the maximum current frequency is P_1, determine the ratio P_1/P.

$2\pi fL = \frac{1}{2\pi fC}$

25 minutes

Test your knowledge

1. a) Write down the equation that relates the de Broglie wavelength to momentum.
   b) A scientist states, 'A proton of mass 1.7×10^{-27} kg is accelerated to a speed at which it has a de Broglie wavelength of no more than 10^{-15} m in order to reveal the structure of nuclei.'

   Supporting your answer with relevant calculations, comment on the validity of this statement.

   $$h = 6.6 \times 10^{-34} \, Js$$

2. Calculate the speed of an electron that has been accelerated from rest through a potential difference of 2V.

   $$electron \ charge = 1.6 \times 10^{-19} \, C$$
   $$electron \ mass = 9.1 \times 10^{-31} \, kg$$

3. Explain why successive tubes of a drift tube accelerator increase in length.

4. Calculate the maximum speed, ignoring relativistic effects, that a proton could reach if it were accelerated by a cyclotron of diameter 200 m in a magnetic field of flux density 0.01 T.

   $$proton \ mass = 1.7 \times 10^{-27} \, kg$$
   $$proton \ charge = 1.6 \times 10^{-19} \, C$$

5. Calculate the magnetic flux density required for a synchrotron of diameter 500 m to accelerate an electron to a speed of 2×10^5 ms^{-1}, ignoring relativistic effects.

   $$electron \ charge = 1.6 \times 10^{-19} \, C$$
   $$electron \ mass = 9.1 \times 10^{-31} \, kg$$

Answers

1 a) $\lambda = h/p$ **b)** at $\lambda = 10^{-15}$ m (e.g. slowest) $v = 3.9 \times 10^8$ ms^{-1}; this is greater than the speed of light. The statement is false. **2** 8.4×10^5 ms^{-1} **3** In exactly the time it takes for a particle to travel through one tube the polarity of the supply potential difference has to reverse, so that the present tube becomes a repelling electrode. Since the electron is getting faster as it progresses, successive tubes need to be longer, otherwise the electron will emerge from the tube before the polarity has reversed. **4** 9.4×10^7 ms^{-1} **5** 4.6×10^{-9} T

 If you got them all right, skip to page 42

Particle Accelerators

25 minutes

Improve your knowledge

1 To reveal the structure of matter on the smallest scales and to form new particles, very high-energy particles are required. These can be created using particle accelerators.

When using particle beams to probe the structure of matter, the smaller the de Broglie wavelength the finer the detail that can be revealed. The de Broglie wavelength is defined as:

$$\lambda = \frac{h}{mv}$$

Therefore, the greater the speed of the particle, the smaller the wavelength.

When particles collide at high energies new particles can be formed. E.g.

$$p + p \rightarrow p + p + \pi^0$$

The kinetic energy of the colliding protons is converted to mass (i.e. the pi zero particle is formed) according to Einstein's mass-energy conversion equation:

$$E = mc^2$$

2 Particles are accelerated in straight lines by linear accelerators or along circular paths by circular accelerators. In both cases particles are accelerated by an electrical potential difference. When a particle carrying charge q moves through an accelerating potential, V, its gain in kinetic energy, KE, is given by:

$$KE = qV$$

$$\Rightarrow \frac{1}{2}mv^2 = qV$$

$$\Rightarrow v = \sqrt{\frac{2qV}{m}}$$

If a particle is to be accelerated along circular paths then a force (centripetal force) has to be applied perpendicular to its motion. This is achieved by applying a magnetic field where:

force due to magnetic field = centripetal force on particle

$$Bqv = \frac{mv^2}{r} \qquad \Rightarrow v = \frac{Bqr}{m}$$

Key points from
AS in a Week

de Broglie
wavelength
            page 74
$E = mc^2$ page 80

h = Planck's constant
m = particle mass
v = particle speed

E = kinetic energy of colliding particles
c = speed of light
m = mass of new particle

m = particle mass
v = particle speed

B = magnetic flux density
r = radius of circular path

Particle Accelerators

In a linear accelerator, the length of the accelerator limits the maximum speed attainable.

In a circular accelerator, the maximum orbital radius and the maximum field strength that can be applied limit the maximum speed.

Particles can be accelerated to speeds close to that of light but they will never reach or exceed it. According to the Special Theory of Relativity, as the particle's speed increases so does its mass, according to the equation:

$$m = \frac{m_0}{\sqrt{1 - \dfrac{v^2}{c^2}}}$$

m = relativistic mass
m_0 = rest mass
v = speed of particle
c = speed of light

Therefore if the particle mass were to reach the speed of light, c, it would have an infinite mass, as the denominator of the quotient would equal zero.

3 The drift tube linac is a linear accelerator that consists of a number of almost fully evacuated tubes. The particles pass through the tubes and are accelerated by potential differences between the tubes.

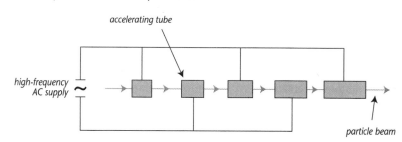

accelerating tube

high-frequency AC supply

particle beam

- While particles are travelling through any one tube they are not accelerated, i.e. they drift, as the whole of an individual tube is at a constant potential difference.

- As a particle leaves a tube the potential difference across the gap should accelerate it forwards towards the next tube, i.e. the previous tube repels the particle and the next one attracts it.

- In exactly the time it takes for a particle to travel through one tube the polarity of the supply potential difference has to reverse, so that the present tube becomes a repelling electrode.

- Since the electron is getting faster as it progresses, successive tubes need to be longer, otherwise the electron will emerge from the tube before the polarity has reversed.

- The drift tube accelerator is normally used to accelerate protons or electrons.

- Speeds close to that of light can be reached. The greater the number of accelerating gaps, the greater the speed.

Particle Accelerators

- Currently the greatest particle energy achievable is 50 keV.
- The beams produced are easy to extract and are well collimated.

The cyclotron consists of two hollow D-shaped metal boxes, narrowly separated in an evacuated chamber. A high-frequency alternating potential difference is applied between the edges to accelerate the particles, and a uniform magnetic field, which is aligned perpendicular to the plane of the Ds, causes the particles to deflect through 180°. An ion source placed at the centre of the Ds produces charged particles, which are often protons.

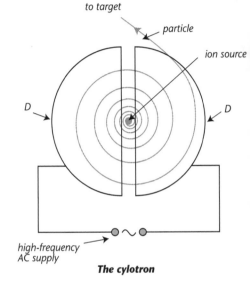

Each time a particle crosses the gap between the Ds it experiences an accelerating force due to the potential difference.

Rearrangement of the equation in point 2 gives:

$$r = \frac{mv}{Bq}$$

Therefore, as the speed of the particle increases so does its radius. Eventually the particle will be directed out of the Ds towards the target.

The distance travelled in one semicircle is given by πr.

$$\text{Time for one semicircle} = t = \frac{\text{distance}}{\text{speed}} = \frac{\pi r}{v} = \frac{\pi m}{Bq}$$

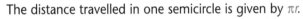

The potential between the Ds reverses twice in one complete orbit, so the period of the AC supply is given by:

$$T = 2t = \frac{2\pi m}{Bq}$$

Therefore the frequency of the supply (cyclotron frequency) is given by:

$$f = \frac{1}{T} = \frac{Bq}{2\pi m}$$

The cyclotron is generally used to accelerate heavy particles and can achieve high speeds without the need for very high potential differences.

Particle Accelerators

5 In a synchrotron a particle is accelerated many times around a circular tube, which is evacuated.

The cavities provide alternating electrical forces to accelerate the particles. The alternating potential differences across the cavities have to be synchronised to coincide with the arrival of the particles.

As with the cyclotron, a perpendicular magnetic field makes the particles move in a circular path and:

$$r = \frac{mv}{Bq}$$

Unlike the cyclotron, the radius of the particle's path is fixed. Therefore, as the speed of the particle increases, the magnetic flux density has to increase proportionally to maintain the fixed orbital radius. Very high currents are therefore required in the electromagnet coils.

In fixed-beam experiments, particles are directed towards a stationary target. In moving-beam experiments the particles and target move in opposite directions.

stationary   *accelerated particle*   *moving (target) beam*   *accelerated particle*

fixed-target collision   *moving-beam collision*

- The total momentum of the particle and target must be conserved (i.e. the same before and after collision).

- For the fixed-target experiment, some of the particle's kinetic energy must be transferred to the stationary target if momentum is to be conserved.

- For the moving-beam experiment, if the particle and target have equal and opposite momentum then their initial total momentum is zero. Therefore, momentum will have been conserved if both particle and target are stationary following collision.

- This means that for moving-beam experiments a greater amount of kinetic energy is available for conversion to new particles.

- Fixed-target experiments offer the advantage that more collisions can be achieved in a given time.

Particle Accelerators

Use your knowledge

1 The diagram below shows a linear particle accelerator.

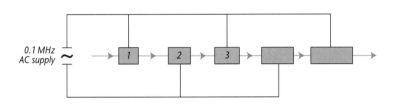

0.1 MHz
AC supply

electron charge =
$1.6 \times 10^{-19} C$
electron mass =
$9.1 \times 10^{-31} kg$

a) Explain why the arrangement is called a *drift* tube accelerator.
   The maximum potential difference between adjacent tubes is 3 kV and an electron
   enters tube 1 with a speed of 2000 ms^{-1} in this example.

Time to pass
through a tube =
supply period/2

b) i) Calculate the lengths of tubes 1, 2 and 3.
   ii) Would it be possible, with a sufficient number of tubes, to
      accelerate an electron to the speed of light? Explain your answer.
   iii) If it was possible, how many tubes would be required?

$gaps = \dfrac{speed\ of\ light}{speed\ gained\ at\ each\ gap}$

2 A cyclotron can be used to accelerate protons to high speeds. If the cyclotron
frequency is 5 MHz, calculate the operational magnetic flux density required.
(Proton mass = 1.7×10^{-27} kg, proton charge = 1.6×10^{-19} C).

$f = \dfrac{Bq}{2\pi m}$

3 The diagram below illustrates a fixed-target particle collision.

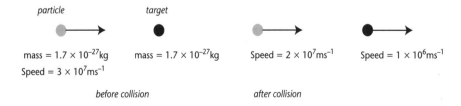

particle   target

mass = 1.7×10^{-27}kg   mass = 1.7×10^{-27}kg   Speed = 2×10^7ms^{-1} Speed = 1×10^6ms^{-1}
Speed = 3×10^7ms^{-1}

before collision   after collision

Calculate the maximum mass of a particle that could be created by this collision.
(Speed of light = 3×10^8ms^{-1})

$\Delta KE = mc^2$

Capacitors

25 minutes

Test your knowledge

1
a) Capacitors are _____ storing devices. The more _____ they can store per 1 V increase in PD, the greater their _____ .

b) A capacitor of capacitance 2 μF has a PD across its plates of 15 V. Calculate the charge held by the capacitor.

2 When a cell is connected across a capacitor, _____ flow from the _____ terminal to one capacitor plate. _____ flow from the other plate to the _____ cell terminal.

3 Determine the energy stored in a capacitor which has a charge of 20 μC and a capacitance of 2 μF.

4 Determine the total capacitance of the arrangements shown below.

a)
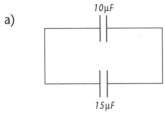

b)

5 Two parallel metal plates have an overlap area of 0.05 m^2 and are separated by 1.5 mm. The relative permittivity of the dielectric between them is 2.5. Determine the capacitance of the arrangement. ($\varepsilon_0 = 8.9 \times 10^{-12}$ Fm^{-1})

6 A capacitor of 25 μF has a potential difference of 15 V across its plates. If the fully charged capacitor is discharged through a resistor of $1 \times 10^5 \, \Omega$, determine the PD across the capacitor after 1.5 s.

Answers

1 a) charge/charge/capacitance b) 30 × 10^{-6} C
2 electrons/negative/Electrons/positive **3** 1 × 10^{-4} J **4** a) 25 μF b) 6 μF
5 7.4 × 10^{-4} μF **6** 8.2 V

 If you got them all right, skip to page 47

Capacitors

40 minutes

Improve your knowledge

1 Capacitors are used to store charge. The capacitance of a capacitor is a measure of its ability to store charge.

Key points from AS in a Week

Current electricity
page 33

- Capacitance is measured in farads (F). Often μF (10^{-6} F) are used.

- All capacitors consist of two parallel metal plates. These sandwich an insulator, known as a dielectric.

- Opposite charges are stored on the plates of the capacitor, resulting in a potential difference across the plates.

- The capacitance (C) is defined as the amount of charge stored per volt increase across the plates.

$$C = \frac{Q}{V}$$

C = capacitance (F)
Q = charge (C) on one plate
V = potential difference (V)

This shows that the voltage across the capacitor is proportional to the charge stored on it.

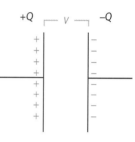

2 Connecting a cell to a capacitor results in flow of electrons from the negative terminal of the cell to the connected capacitor plate. Electrons flow, at the same rate from the opposing plate to the positive terminal of the cell, resulting in a build-up of equal and opposite charges on the plates. When the capacitor is charged to its full capacity, current no longer flows.

If the charged capacitor is then connected to a complete circuit, the electrons will flow in the opposite direction, from the negative plate around the circuit onto the positive plate, neutralising the positive charge. When there is no voltage across the capacitor it stores no charge, i.e. it is fully discharged.

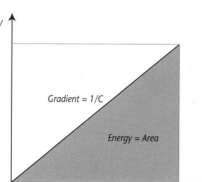

3 A charged capacitor stores energy, i.e. the stored charge could be used to light a flash bulb. The energy is given by:

$$E = \frac{1}{2}QV = \frac{1}{2}CV^2 = \frac{Q^2}{2C}$$

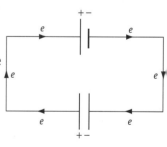

Gradient = 1/C

Energy = Area

Capacitors

4 The total capacitance of a parallel arrangement of capacitors is given by:

$$C = C_1 + C_2 + ...$$

The total capacitance of a series arrangement of capacitors is given by:

$$\frac{1}{C} = \frac{1}{C_1} + \frac{1}{C_2} + ...$$

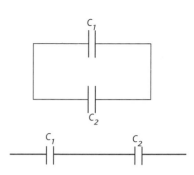

5 For a parallel-plate capacitor, the capacitance is dependent upon the:

- plate separation (d)
- area of plate overlap (A)
- type of dielectric material between the plates. This is indicated by the material's relative permittivity (ε_r). The permittivity is defined as $\varepsilon = \varepsilon_0 \varepsilon_r$ (Fm^{-1}), where ε_0 is the permittivity of a vacuum ($\varepsilon_0 = 8.9 \times 10^{-12} Fm^{-1}$).

$$C = \frac{\varepsilon A}{d}$$

6 If a capacitor discharges through a resistor, the charge stored decreases exponentially.

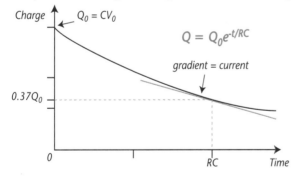

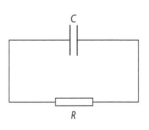

The voltage across the capacitor will decrease as the charge decreases, as they are proportional (Q = CV).

$$V = V_0 e^{-t/RC}$$

R = parallel resistance
C = capacitance
Q = charge remaining after time t
Q_0 = initial charge at time $t = 0$
V = voltage across the capacitor after time t
V_0 = initial voltage at time $t = 0$
I = current in circuit after time t
I_0 = initial current at time $t = 0$

Capacitors

The gradient of the charge-time graph gives the current, which also falls in a similar way.

The area under the current-time graph gives the charge that has flowed from the capacitor during the time interval.

An exponential decay means there is a constant fractional change in a quantity over a given time period.

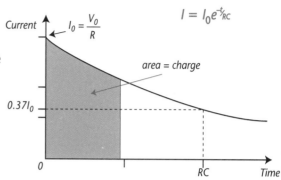

- The average time for the quantity to decrease to half its initial value is called the half-life ($T_{1/2}$). After two half-lifes have passed ($t = 2T_{1/2}$), the quantity has decreased to a quarter of its initial value, and to one eighth after $3T_{1/2}$ (see figure).

- The average time for the quantity to decrease to 0.37 ($= 1/e$) of its initial value is called the time constant (τ). The time constant is defined as:

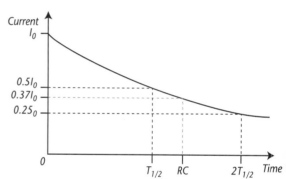

$$\tau = RC$$

R = resistance (Ω)
C = capacitance (F)
τ = time constant (s)

The time constant is larger for larger R because the current is less so it takes longer for the current to fall. It is larger for larger C because there is more charge stored so it takes longer for the capacitor to discharge by a given fraction.

The time constant relates directly to the half-life by:

$$T_{1/2} = \tau \ln 2$$

These times can be read from discharge graphs, as shown above.

Capacitors

Use your knowledge

1 The switch in the diagram is initially connected to position A, fully charging the capacitor. The capacitor is discharged through the resistor by switching to position B. Calculate:

a) The charge stored on the fully charged capacitor.

b) The energy stored by the fully charged capacitor.

c) The time constant of the discharge circuit.

d) The PD across the plates of the capacitor 55.5 s after the switch is connected to B.

e) The charge held by the capacitors after this time.

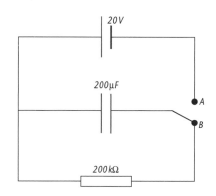

$Q = CV$

$V = V_O e^{-t/RC}$

2 a) Calculate the total capacitance of the network below.

b) If the terminals of a 12 V cell are placed across A and B determine:

   i) The total charge stored on the capacitor network.

   ii) The total energy stored on the capacitor network.

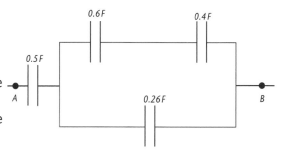

3 Two parallel metal plates are separated by an air gap d and have an area of overlap A. A potential difference V across the plates results in stored energy E. When the separation is halved and the gap is filled with a dielectric of relative permittivity 2.5, the potential difference of V results in stored energy E_1. What is the ratio E_1/E?

Unknown values will cancel in ratio.

30 minutes

Test your knowledge

1
a) Calculate the activity of a pure sample of uranium containing 2.0×10^{10} nuclei, with a decay constant of $4.9 \times 10^{-18} s^{-1}$.
b) If a sample of radioactive material initially has 3.7×10^7 unstable nuclei, how many would remain after 28 hours if the decay constant is $1.5 \times 10^{-4} s^{-1}$?

2
a) Calculate the half-life of a radioactive sample with a decay constant of $2.3 \times 10^{-7} s^{-1}$.
b) If a sample initially contains N_0 undecayed atoms, how many would remain following four half-lives?

3
a) Define nuclear fission.
b) Calculate the energy released in the fusion reaction:
$$^2_1H + ^3_1H \rightarrow ^4_2He + ^1_0n$$

masses:
H2 = 2.014102u
H3 = 3.016049u
He4 = 4.002604u
neutron = 1.0087u
1u = 1.661×10^{-27}kg,
c = $3 \times 10^8 ms^{-1}$

4
An N–Z curve, such as that shown here, can be used to predict the stability and nature of decay of a nucleus. Which type of decay is likely to occur for nuclei in positions a), b) and c)?

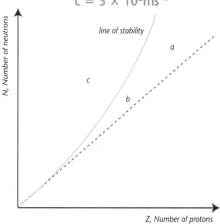

5
In a nuclear fission reactor, _____ of U-235 is induced by bombardment with _____ . A _____ reaction takes place and if left unchecked _____ could occur. Absorption of neutrons by _____ rods prevents this occurring.

 If you got them all right, skip to page 53

The Nucleus and Radioactivity

25 minutes

Improve your knowledge

Check the following topics covered in 'The Nucleus and Radioactivity' chapter in *AS Physics in a Week*.

Key points from
AS in a Week

The nucleus and
radiocativity
pages 78–83

- Rutherford's alpha-particle scattering experiment
- Nuclear equations
- Binding energy and $E = mc^2$
- Nuclear stability
- Properties of ionising radiation
- Background radiation
- Half-life and activity

1 The disintegration (decay) of nuclei is a random process, but the more nuclei present in a sample the greater the chance of detecting a disintegration.

- The number of disintegrations per second is known as the activity ($\frac{dN}{dT}$) of the sample:

$$\frac{dN}{dt} = -\lambda N \quad \text{where } \lambda = \text{decay constant (s}^{-1}\text{)}.$$

- The minus sign indicates that N decreases with time.

The number of unstable nuclei remaining in a sample after a given time is:

$$N = N_0 e^{-\lambda t}$$

where N = number of nuclei after time t
N_0 = number at $t = 0$

- Also:

$$I = I_0 e^{-\lambda t}$$
$$A = A_0 e^{-\lambda t}$$

where I = measured intensity
A = activity.

2 While the underlying nature of radioactive decay is random, we can make accurate predictions about the behaviour of a sample containing a large number of nuclei, such as its half-life. The half-life ($T_{1/2}$) is defined as the time taken for half the unstable nuclei of a sample to decay.

The Nucleus and Radioactivity

If we apply this to the equation in point 1, i.e.

$$N = N_0 e^{-\lambda t}$$

After one half-life: $\quad N = \dfrac{N_0}{2} \quad$ and $t = T_{1/2}$

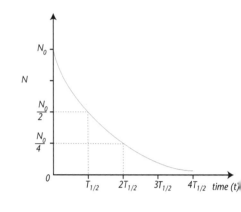

$$\Rightarrow \frac{N_0}{2} = N_0 e^{-\lambda\, T_{1/2}} \qquad \Rightarrow \frac{1}{2} = e^{-\lambda\, T_{1/2}}$$

Taking natural logarithms of both sides:

$$\ln\frac{1}{2} = \ln e^{-\lambda\, T_{1/2}}$$

$$\Rightarrow -\ln 2 = -\lambda\, T_{1/2} \quad \Rightarrow T_{1/2} = \frac{\ln 2}{\lambda}$$

The half-life of a sample containing one kind of isotope is constant. A plot of N against t is an exponential decay curve.

3 Dividing the binding energy (BE) of a nucleus by the nucleon number gives the BE per nucleon. This reveals the relative stability of the nucleus.

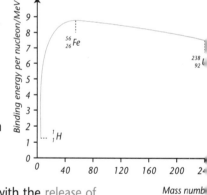

- The greater the BE per nucleon, the more stable the nucleus (less likely to change).

- A plot of BE/nucleon against nucleon number is shown in the diagram.

- Nuclei near the peak of the graph have the greatest BE per nucleon and are therefore the most stable. Iron (Fe) is one of the most stable.

Nuclear fission occurs when a heavy nucleus splits into lighter nuclei with the release of energy. The lighter nuclei will be more stable than the original nucleus (positioned further up the peak) as they have a greater BE per nucleon.

- Fission occurs with very heavy nuclei to the right of the peak.

Nuclear fusion occurs when two light nuclei join to form a heavier, more stable nucleus with the release of energy. The fusion product has a greater BE per nucleon than the original nuclei (further up the peak).

- Fusion occurs with very light nuclei to the left of the peak.

Units of mass and energy commonly used in nuclear problems are:

- The atomic mass unit: $1\,u = 1.661 \times 10^{-27}\,kg$

- The electron volt: $1\,eV = 1.6 \times 10^{-19}\,J \quad$ where $1\,u = 932\,MeV$.

The Nucleus and Radioactivity

4

A plot of number of neutrons against number of protons, i.e. an *N–Z* curve, can be used to predict the stability of a nucleus

Low-*Z* nuclei (*Z* < 20): *N* = *Z* are stable.

High-*Z* nuclei (*Z* > 20): *N* > *Z* are stable.

These stable nuclei lie on the line of stability.

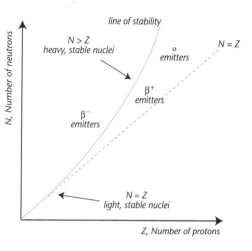

* Unstable nuclei above the line of stability have an excess of neutrons. They become more stable by β⁻ decay; a neutron changes into a proton and an electron.

$$_{0}^{1}n \rightarrow {}_{1}^{1}p + {}_{-1}^{0}e^{-}$$

* Unstable nuclei below the line of stability have an excess of protons. They become more stable by β⁺ decay; a proton changes into a neutron and a positron.

$$_{1}^{1}p \rightarrow {}_{0}^{1}n + {}_{+1}^{0}e^{+}$$

* Heavy nuclei (Z > 82) below the line of stability decay by alpha particle emission.

5

* Fission of U-235 (uranium 235) most commonly fuels a nuclear power station.

* U-235 is relatively stable, but fission can by induced by firing neutrons at the uranium atoms. A neutron is absorbed and the U-235 becomes unstable and undergoes fission.

* High-speed fission fragments and neutrons are produced. Their kinetic energy is converted into thermal energy by collisions with the moderator. The moderator is most often made from graphite or water.

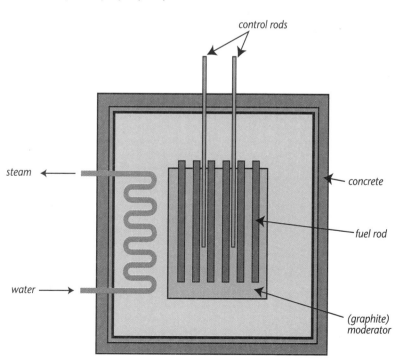

- These neutrons (on average 2.5 are produced per fission) can collide with other uranium atoms, again causing fission and the production of more neutrons. A chain reaction occurs.

- The neutrons produced have too great a speed to cause further fission. The moderator slows them to the optimum speed.

- If the fission chain reaction was left to continue freely, energy would be produced a rate that increased exponentially. Meltdown would occur.

- Control rods (boron-coated steel) absorb some of the neutrons, ideally leaving one produced per fission. This limits the rate of energy production, which can be controlled by varying the depth of the rods within the reactor.

Use your knowledge

1 The nuclei in a radioactive sample of 2.0×10^{40} polonium nuclei decay according to the equation below:

$$^{218}_{X}\text{Po} \rightarrow {}^{214}_{82}\text{Pb} + {}^{Y}_{2}Z$$

a) Determine values of X and Y.
b) Identify the ionising radiation Z.
c) The half-life of Po is 1.2×10^7 s. Determine the time elapsed when the number of remaining Po nuclei falls to 1.2×10^3.

The total nucleon number (and proton number) must be the same on both sides of the equation.

Use $N = N_0 e^{-\lambda t}$ and then take natural logarithms of both sides.

2 The measured activity of a source emitting gamma radiation is found to decrease as the detector is moved away from the source. It is established that the measured activity (A) is related to the separation between the source and detector (r) by:

$$A \propto \frac{1}{r^2}$$

Calculate the activity at 2 m at t = 30 s. Doubling the separation will quarter the measured activity.

If at $r = 2$ m the activity is measured to be 5×10^{10} s^{-1}, what would the activity be 30 s later, 4 m away? ($T_{1/2} = 18$ s)

3 State the difference between nuclear fusion and nuclear fission.

4 Sketch a graph with labelled axes of nucleon number against binding energy per nucleon. Indicate on your graph the positions of $^{1}_{1}\text{H}$, $^{56}_{26}\text{Fe}$, $^{238}_{92}\text{U}$. Label the regions where fission and fusion occur.

5 Thermal nuclear fission reactors can produce very large amounts of energy for a small mass of fuel.
a) Which uranium isotope is most commonly used in a nuclear fission reactor?
b) How is fission of this isotope induced?
c) How can an out-of-control chain reaction be prevented and the rate of energy production controlled?

Thermodynamics

10 minutes

Test your knowledge

1 a) _____ is a measure of the average translational kinetic energy of the particles in a substance. When there is no net transfer of heat between two bodies, they are said to be in _____ _____ . The thermodynamic temperature scale is a theoretical scale, with units _____ .

b) $pV = nRT$ is the _____ _____ equation, where p is the pressure, V the _____ , n the _____ ___ _____ , R the molar gas constant and T the _____ for the gas.

c) An ideal gas is one which obeys the _____ _____ equation and the _____ theory. Generally, the _____ energy of a body is defined as the sum of its kinetic and potential energy. However, an ideal gas only has _____ energy.

2 A volume of 3×10^3 ml of water at 24 °C is placed in the freezer. If it takes 80 minutes for all the water to freeze, calculate the rate at which the freezer extracts heat from the water. Assume the heat capacity of the bag is negligible.

Density of water = 1.0 $\times 10^3$ kgm^{-3}

Specific heat capacity of water = 4.2 $\times 10^3$ JK^{-1}kg^{-1}

Specific latent heat of fusion of ice = 3.4 $\times 10^5$ Jkg^{-1}

1 m^3 = 10^6 ml

3 What is a heat engine? Explain why it is desirable to make turbine blades that will operate at higher temperatures to improve the efficiency of thermal power stations.

Thermodynamics

Improve your knowledge

 The Zeroth Law: Thermal Equilibrium and Temperature.

Key points from
AS in a Week

Heat   pages 59–63

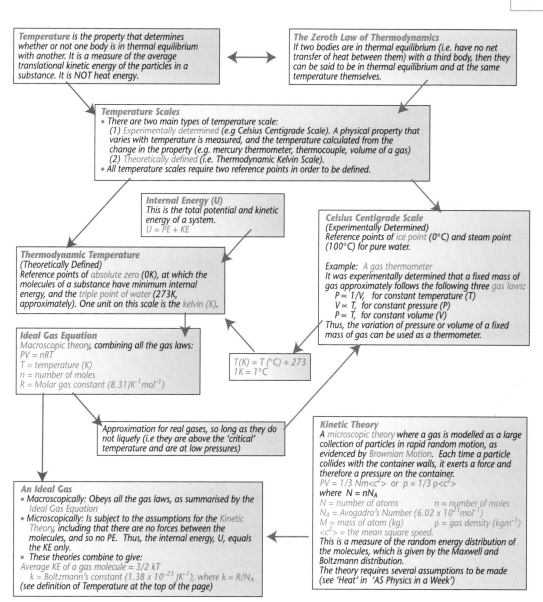

Temperature is the property that determines whether or not one body is in thermal equilibrium with another. It is a measure of the average translational kinetic energy of the particles in a substance. It is NOT heat energy.

The Zeroth Law of Thermodynamics
If two bodies are in thermal equilibrium (i.e. have no net transfer of heat between them) with a third body, then they can be said to be in thermal equilibrium and at the same temperature themselves.

Temperature Scales
- There are two main types of temperature scale:
  (1) *Experimentally determined* (e.g Celsius Centigrade Scale). A physical property that varies with temperature is measured, and the temperature calculated from the change in the property (e.g. mercury thermometer, thermocouple, volume of a gas)
  (2) *Theoretically defined* (i.e. Thermodynamic Kelvin Scale).
- All temperature scales require two reference points in order to be defined.

Internal Energy (U)
This is the total potential and kinetic energy of a system.
$U = PE + KE$

Celsius Centigrade Scale
(Experimentally Determined)
Reference points of *ice point* (0°C) and steam point (100°C) for pure water.

Example: A gas thermometer
It was experimentally determined that a fixed mass of gas approximately follows the following three *gas laws*:
$P \propto 1/V$,   for constant temperature (T)
$V \propto T$,   for constant pressure (P)
$P \propto T$,   for constant volume (V)
Thus, the variation of pressure or volume of a fixed mass of gas can be used as a thermometer.

Thermodynamic Temperature
(Theoretically Defined)
Reference points of *absolute zero* (0K), at which the molecules of a substance have minimum internal energy, and the *triple point of water* (273K, approximately). One unit on this scale is the *kelvin (K)*.

Ideal Gas Equation
Macroscopic theory, combining all the gas laws:
$PV = nRT$
T = temperature (K)
n = number of moles
R = Molar gas constant (8.31$JK^{-1}mol^{-1}$)

$T(K) = T(°C) + 273$
$1K = 1°C$

Approximation for real gases, so long as they do not liquefy (i.e they are above the 'critical' temperature and are at low pressures)

Kinetic Theory
A *microscopic theory* where a gas is modelled as a large collection of particles in rapid random motion, as evidenced by *Brownian Motion*. Each time a particle collides with the container walls, it exerts a force and therefore a pressure on the container.
$PV = 1/3 \, Nm<c^2>$ or $p = 1/3 \, \rho<c^2>$
where $N = nN_A$
N = number of atoms n = number of moles
N_A = Avogadro's Number (6.02 x $10^{23}mol^{-1}$)
M = mass of atom (kg) ρ = gas density (kgm^{-3})
$<c^2>$ = the mean square speed
This is a measure of the random energy distribution of the molecules, which is given by the Maxwell and Boltzmann distribution.
The theory requires several assumptions to be made (see 'Heat' in 'AS Physics in a Week')

An Ideal Gas
- *Macroscopically:* Obeys all the gas laws, as summarised by the Ideal Gas Equation
- *Microscopically:* Is subject to the assumptions for the *Kinetic Theory*, including that there are no forces between the molecules, and so no PE. Thus, the internal energy, U, equals the KE only.
- These theories combine to give:
  Average KE of a gas molecule = 3/2 kT
  k = Boltzmann's constant (1.38 x 10^{-23} JK^{-1}), where $k = R/N_A$
  (see definition of Temperature at the top of the page)

Thermodynamics

2 The First Law of thermodynamics

This is a statement of the principle of conservation of energy: Energy can never be created or destroyed, only transformed.

$$\Delta Q = \Delta U + \Delta W^{by} \qquad \text{(First Law)}$$

- ΔQ: Heat energy is a flow of energy between bodies at different temperatures and is measured positively if energy flows into the system. Energy is exchanged until thermal equilibrium is reached (i.e. the rate of heat flow into each body is equal to the rate of heat flow out).
- ΔW^{by}: Work done by a system is measured positively if energy is transferred from the system to the surroundings by:
  1) Change in volume (e.g. a gas at constant temperature). If a system (e.g. a gas) expands, it does work as it pushes the surrounding air.
  $$\Delta W = p\Delta V$$
  $p = $ pressure
  $\Delta V = $ change in volume

  2) Electrical energy (e.g. a heater). The amount of energy transferred (the work done) in an electrical circuit is given by:
  $$\Delta W = IV\Delta t$$
  $I = $ current through the component
  $V = $ the p.d. across the device
  $\Delta t = $ the time the current flows for

- ΔU: Change in internal energy can be due to a change in either, or both, the kinetic (ΔKE) and potential energies (ΔPE).
  $$\Delta U = \Delta KE + \Delta PE$$

ΔKE: Kinetic energy As the motion of the atoms increases, so does the temperature. The energy required to raise the temperature of 1 kg of a material by 1 °C is the specific heat capacity (c):

$\Delta Q = $ change in or transfer of energy
$m = $ mass of the body
$c = $ specific heat capacity of the body
$C = $ heat capacity of the body
$\Delta T = $ temperature change

$$\Delta Q = mc\Delta T = C\Delta T$$

(NB c will differ for a material when in different states.) In the case of an ideal gas, this is the only way in which the internal energy can change.

ΔPE: Potential energy is stored in a material's bonds. If it changes state, the PE will change (e.g. evaporation, boiling). If the temperature remains constant while the PE changes (e.g. boiling or melting) the energy required to melt or vaporise 1 kg of a substance at a constant temperature is the specific latent heat of fusion/vaporisation (l).

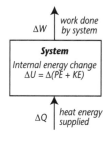

Example of the First Law:
1 kg of water at 100 °C changes into steam at atmospheric pressure, while held in a cylinder by a free-sliding piston.
ρ_w (water) at 100 °C = 960 kgm^{-3}
ρ_s (steam) at 100 °C = 0.59 kgm^{-3}
atmospheric pressure = 1.10×10^5 Pa
l (vap) water = 2.26×10^6 Jkg^{-1}
$\Delta Q > 0$, as heat is supplied.
$\Delta KE = 0$, as temperature is constant
$\Delta PE > 0$, due to the change of state
$\Delta U = \Delta PE = ml = + 2.3 \times 10^6$
$\Delta W > 0$, as the system expands
$\Delta W = P\Delta V = Pm\,(1/\rho_s - 1/\rho_w) = + 1.7 \times 10^5$ J
$\Delta Q = \Delta U + \Delta W = + 2.5 \times 10^6$

Thermodynamics

$$\Delta Q = ml$$

N.B. l for a material will be different for fusion, vaporisation and sublimation (solid to gas).

Applications of internal energy

The graph shows how the temperature of water varies as it is heated at a constant rate, assuming the system is perfectly lagged (insulated). In the lab, we do not have perfect lagging and so obtain curves rather than straight lines.

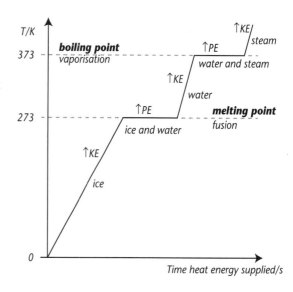

In regions where the temperature is rising, the heat energy increases the kinetic energy of the molecules. In time periods where the line is flat (constant temperature) ΔQ increases the PE of the molecules as they change state. Either way ΔU increases.

The power, or the amount of energy input per second, for a perfectly lagged system is given by:

$$\text{Power} = \frac{\Delta Q}{\Delta t} = mc\frac{\Delta T}{\Delta t}$$

Application of 'power equation': This is usually required in questions where water is flowing at a constant rate past a heater in order to raise its temperature by a certain amount.

An alternative view of the First Law

It is possible to alter the internal energy of a system by transferring energy by either: (1) heating ΔQ and/or (2) doing work on the system ΔW^{on}. Thus, the First Law can be rewritten as:

$$\Delta U = \Delta Q - \Delta W^{by} = \Delta Q + \Delta W^{on}$$

where, ΔW^{on} is the work done on the system, rather than the work done by the system, ΔW^{by}.

P–V Diagrams

Changes to gas systems are usually represented by pressure–volume diagrams. The three gas laws are plotted on the P–V diagram, and explained for an *ideal gas*. It is important to understand the terms used and how they relate to the First Law.

The work done is shown by the area under the P–V curve. Thus, for a closed-loop cycle (e.g. engine cycle), the total work done by the gas per cycle is given by the area enclosed by the loop.

Thermodynamics

Other terms to know:

Adiabatic ($\Delta Q = 0$). No heat flow. All work done is at the expense of the internal energy, so the gas cools on expansion ($\Delta W = -\Delta U$).

Isolated ($\Delta Q = \Delta W = 0$). No heat flow or work done. Thus the internal energy remains constant: PE may be converted into KE and vice versa only ($\Delta U = 0 \Rightarrow \Delta PE = -\Delta KE$).

3 The Second Law of thermodynamics

In order to drive heat energy from one place to another, a temperature difference is required. The flow of heat from a hot body to a cold one can be used to create some useful work output, e.g. turning turbine blades in a thermal power station. This is called a heat engine – a device that converts heat into useful work.

ΔU

All heat becomes internal energy (i.e. KE) and the T rises

ΔQ

Isovolumetric (const. V)
P/T = constant
$\Delta W = 0; \Delta Q = \Delta U$

Work = Area under P–V plot
Energy/cycle = area enclosed

ΔW

All heat goes to do work in pushing back the atmosphere. The system remains at constant T (i.e. KE).

$\Delta U = 0; \Delta Q = \Delta W$

Isothermal (const. T)
PV = constant

ΔQ

ΔW

Isobaric (const. P)
V/T = constant

ΔU

Some heat increases U (i.e. the KE), and the remainder pushes back the atmosphere
$\Delta Q = \Delta U + \Delta W$

ΔQ

The Second Law states that there is an upper limit to the efficiency of a heat engine: 'No continually operating heat engine can take heat energy from a source and completely transform it into useful work.' As the engine is based on the flow of heat from a hot body to a cold one, some heat must always flow to the cold sink, otherwise the flow (and thus the engine) will stop. For maximum efficiency, we require the greatest temperature difference between the source and sink (see diagram). Eventually all the heat energy will be dissipated into the internal energy of the surrounding.

The opposite of a heat engine is a heat pump, which pushes heat energy from a cold body to a hot one. Examples include refrigerators, freezers and air conditioners.

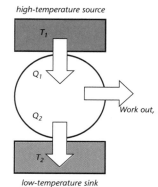

high-temperature source

T_1

Q_1

Q_2

Work out,

T_2

low-temperature sink

conservation of energy (First Law)
$Q_1 = Q2 + W \Rightarrow W = Q_1 - Q_2$
maximum efficiency (Second Law)
$= W/Q_1 = 1 - Q_2/Q_1 = 1 - T_2/T_1$

Conservation of energy (First Law)
$$Q_1 = Q_2 + W \Rightarrow W = Q_1 - Q_2$$
Maximum Efficiency (Second Law)
$$= W/Q_1 = 1 - Q_2/Q_1 = 1 - T_2/T_1$$

Thermodynamics

Use your knowledge

1 Under what two conditions does a gas behave as an ideal gas? Consider such a gas of volume $V_A = 1000\,cm^3$ at a pressure $P_A = 1.10 \times 10^5\,Pa$ and temperature $T_A = 300\,K$ contained in the chamber as shown. The gas undergoes a sequence of changes as shown on the pressure–volume diagram.

a) Along AB the gas is heated to 400 K at constant pressure. What is the new volume at B, V_B?

b) The gas is then compressed while at this temperature to point C, with pressure P_C. What name is given to describe such a change? Calculate the new pressure P_C.

c) Describe the change in the gas from C to A.

d) State how the work done on the gas for the full cycle may be found from the PV diagram.

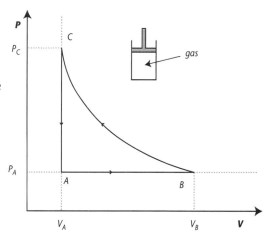

2 A fridge uses a pump to move energy from the inside of the fridge to the outside. In one week of operation the pump uses 20 MJ of energy to drive 60 MJ of energy from inside the fridge.

a) (i) State the First Law of thermodynamics, defining all symbols used.

(ii) How much energy flows out of the fridge?

(iii) State the Second Law of thermodynamics.

(iv) Why is a pump required to pump energy from inside the fridge to the outside?

b) Calculate the power flow through the fridge walls.

Quantum Duality

15 minutes

Test your knowledge

1 Complete the table with appropriate experiments to demonstrate the wave and particle nature of light and an electron.

	Wave nature	Particle nature
Light	Young's slits Experiment	ii)
Electron	i)	iii)

Charge on an electron = 1.6 × 10⁻¹⁹ C

2 a) Define the 'de Broglie wavelength' for a particle.

b) An alpha particle is emitted during a radioactive decay with kinetic energy of 4.0 MeV.

   i) Calculate its speed (neglect relativistic effects).

   ii) What is its 'associated wavelength'?

   iii) Could this alpha particle be used to probe the structure of an atom, a nucleus, or neither? Explain your answer.

Mass of an alpha particle = 6.4 × 10⁻²⁷ kg

Planck's constant = 6.63 × 10⁻³⁴ Js

3 Millikan's oil drop experiment is used to determine the charge on the _____ . He concluded that charge always came in _____ multiples of _____ coulombs. In doing this, he established the _____ nature of the electron.

4 a) Write out Einstein's photoelectric equation for the photoelectric effect for light. Define all the terms used.

b) Name an experiment that is used to verify Einstein's photoelectric equation.

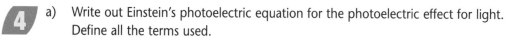

Answers

 If you got them all right, skip to page 65

Quantum Duality

20 minutes

Improve your knowledge

1 Wave–particle duality is used to describe the behaviour of things that cannot completely be described by a wave or particle model alone – but require both. Whether we observe the particle or wave nature depends on the experiment and observations made.

There are two main examples:

- the electron, usually considered a particle, has been shown to exhibit wave behaviour

- light, usually considered a wave, can exhibit particle-like properties.

This seems contradictory! What you need to accept is that the *ideas* of light (or the electron) being wave-like *or* particle-like are merely different models to help us explain the behaviour of light (or the electron) – neither is an exact description of what light (or the electron) itself is! We say that it has a dual nature.

Key points from AS in a Week

Quantum physics
page 71

Basic wave properties
page 46

Further waves
page 53

The table outlines some experiments demonstrating the particle and wave nature for both light and the electron. Further details of some of these experiments are given in Section 3, for electrons, and Section 4, for light.

	Wave-like character	*Particle-like character*
Light	• Young's slits experiment • Diffracts, reflects and refracts	• Photoelectric effect • Millikan's verification of Einstein's equation
Electron	• Diffraction and interference • Atomic emission spectra	• Millikan's experiment for the quantisation of charge

2 Electromagnetic radiation, which includes light, is shown to exhibit particle-like properties, as demonstrated by the photoelectric effect where light of frequency f is considered to be a stream of 'particles', known as photons, with energy:

$$E = hf$$

E = photon energy (J)
h = Planck's constant (6.63×10^{-34} Js)
f = frequency (Hz)

Matter is made up of particles. De Broglie suggested all particles can be considered to exhibit wave-like behaviour under suitable conditions. Therefore, neutrons and hydrogen atoms, for example, can be considered to have a 'wave-like' behaviour – indeed they can be diffracted! Any particle with momentum p has an associated 'de Broglie wavelength' given by:

$$\lambda = \frac{h}{p} = \frac{h}{mv}$$

λ = (wave) wavelength (m)
h = Planck's constant (6.63×10^{-34} Js)
p = (particle) momentum (kgms^{-1})
m = (particle) mass (kg)
v = (particle) speed (ms^{-1})

This model predicts that the associated wavelength for large (i.e. macroscopic) bodies will be very small, due to their large masses, and so their associated wave behaviour is very difficult to observe.

To calculate the associated wavelength for a particle, of mass m and charge q, which has been accelerated from rest through a potential difference, V, to a speed of v, equate the gain in kinetic energy ($\frac{1}{2}mv^2$) to the drop in electrical energy (qV). This gives

$$v = \sqrt{\frac{2qV}{m}}$$ Substituting into de Broglie: $$\lambda = \frac{h}{p} = \frac{h}{\sqrt{2mqV}}$$

What does the 'associated wavelength' for a particle mean?
The amplitude of the 'associated wave' varies in space and time. The square of this amplitude at any given point in space and time is proportional to the probability of the associated 'particle' being at that point. Only when we make an observation do we reveal the 'particle' at one particular point.

Equivalently, for electromagnetic radiation (e.g. light), the probability of a photon (light particle) being at a particular point is proportional to the intensity of the 'light wave' at that point, which itself is proportional to the square of the amplitude of the light wave.

3 The electron has been shown to exhibit wave-like properties such as diffraction and interference. The diffraction pattern produced is a set of concentric circles (see diagram). The deflection of the diffracted electrons can be calculated to provide information about the spacing of atoms in solids. In this manner, the wave-like behaviour of electrons can be used in TEM (tunnelling electron microscopy). In addition, atomic emission spectra give further evidence to support the wave model for electrons, which is applied to the operation of lasers.

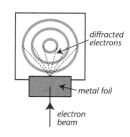

Evidence for the particle nature of the electron was mainly gained through Millikan's oil drop experiment in which he determined that charge came in 'lumps' of 1.6×10^{-19} coulombs (i.e. the electron charge, e).

Experiment: A fine mist of charged oil droplets was formed using an atomiser. These were injected between two parallel metal plates and observed by reflecting light through a low-powered microscope, which incorporated a scale so the terminal velocity of a droplet could be calculated by timing its fall through a known distance.

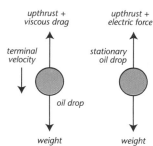

Measurements: There are essentially two measurements that allowed Millikan to calculate the charge on a drop. (1) The terminal velocity of the drop when weight is opposed by the upthrust and viscous drag forces. (2) The voltage required across the plates in order to hold a drop stationary.

Results: The charges were always integral multiples of 1.6×10^{-19} C.

Conclusion: Electric charge can never exist in fractions of this amount, and the electron charge is 1.6×10^{-19} C. Thus Millikan established the particle nature of the electron.

4 There is much experimental evidence for the wave nature of light, but most renowned is the Young's slits experiment.

The particle view of light describes light as consisting of a stream of particles, called photons, each with an energy related to the frequency, hf. The photoelectric effect requires the explanation of light as a particle, where light photons of energy hf liberate electrons from the surface of a metal. This was summarised by Einstein's photoelectric equation.

Einstein's photoelectric equation: $$KE_{max} = hf - \phi$$

Millikan performed the following experiment to verify Einstein's equation and measure Planck's constant (h) and metal work functions (ϕ).

KE_{max} = maximum kinetic energy of photoelectron
h = Planck's constant
f = frequency (Hz)
ϕ = work function of metal

Experiment: A selection of three metals are mounted on a rotating table. The tube is evacuated to prevent any surface oxidation of the elements, which are very reactive. Any oxide that did form was removed with a mounted knife. A target metal was irradiated with *monochromatic* light, which was above the metal's threshold frequency. As glass absorbs these UV frequencies, and quartz does not, the chamber has a quartz window. The photoemitted electrons were then collected by the cathode (C), which completed the circuit as shown and so a current was measured by the sensitive electrometer.

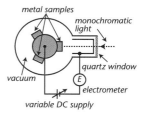

Measurements: For a variety of metals, the stopping voltage (see below) was recorded over a range of light frequencies.

Theory: If the metal was given a positive potential by using a variable DC supply, the photoemitted electrons were slowed down. Electrons with low kinetic energies therefore did not reach the cathode, and so the current dropped. When the potential was increased so that even the electrons with the maximum kinetic energy were unable to reach the cathode, the current fell to zero. The minimum potential required to reduce the current to zero is the stopping voltage. This occurs when all the electron's kinetic energy is used to do work against the electric field:

$eV = KE_{max}$. Using Einstein's equation, this becomes:

$$V = \frac{h}{e}f - \frac{\phi}{e}$$

Results: For all metals, a plot of V against f is a straight line.

Conclusions: There are three main conclusions:

- Einstein's equation is correct, as the plot is a straight line.

- Planck's constant (h) can be determined from the gradient of the line, which is (h/e), where e is the charge on an electron (see above for determination of e). All metals will have the same gradient (i.e. Planck's constant is constant).

- The metal work function, ϕ, is determined from the V-axis intercept, which is $-(\phi/e)$. Different metals have different intercepts.

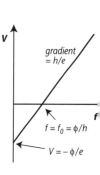

Quantum Duality

Use your knowledge

 1

a) Define the 'de Broglie' wavelength.
b) Explain its significance.
c) A particle of mass m and charge q, is accelerated from rest through a potential difference, V, to a speed v. Show that its de Broglie wavelength is given by:

$$\lambda = \frac{h}{\sqrt{2mqV}}$$

d) Calculate the wavelength for:
   i) an electron accelerated through 500V and
   ii) a car of mass 1000kg moving at 10ms⁻¹.

2

a) Light displays wave–particle duality. What is meant by this?
b) How does Young's slits experiment demonstrate the wave nature of light?
c) The photoelectric effect demonstrates the particle nature of light. It is described by Einstein's photoelectric equation:
   $KE_{max} = hf - \phi$
   Millikan's experiment is used to verify Einstein's equation. Describe this experiment, including a description of the apparatus, measurements and how the data is analysed.
d) The plot shows some data obtained by Millikan's experiment. Use this data to calculate:
   i) Planck's constant.
   ii) The metal work function.

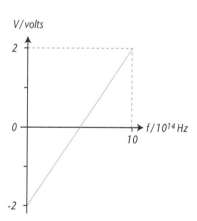

Gain in KE = loss in PE

$$\frac{1}{2}mv^2 = qV$$

Then use this value of v in the de Broglie equation.

Electron charge = $1.6 \times 10^{-19}C$

Electron mass = $9.1 \times 10^{-31}kg$

Planck's constant = $6.63 \times 10^{-34}Js$

Diffraction of light only occurs when the wavelength is similar to the size of the gap.

Astrophysics

25 minutes

Test your knowledge

1 Stars are formed from collapsing _____ of dust and _____ that comprise mostly _____ with a little helium. If the collapsing mass is greater than _____ solar masses then the temperature may reach 1.5×10^7 K and fusion of _____ to _____ will occur.

2 a) What causes a main sequence star to become unstable initially?
b) List the two steps in the Sun's evolution following its time as a main sequence star.

3 a) Suggest a suitable location for a telescope that detects:
i) gamma rays
ii) visible light
b) For a telescope with an objective lens diameter of 5 cm which operates at a wavelength of 600 nm, determine the minimum angular separation of stars that can be resolved.

4 Use Wein's law to determine the wavelength at which a star emits the majority of its power if it has a surface temperature of 10 000 K.

5 Observations of a star at six-monthly intervals generate a parallax angle of 0.1°. Determine the separation between Earth and the star.

6 A star viewed from the surface of the Earth has an apparent magnitude 6 and an absolute magnitude of 2. Determine its distance in parsecs from the Earth.

7 State Hubble's law.
A galaxy at a distance, d, from earth is observed to be receding at a velocity, v. Express the age of the universe in terms of v and d.

Answers

1 clouds/gas/hydrogen/100/hydrogen/helium **2** a) core hydrogen runs out b) red giant to white dwarf **3** a) i) satellite ii) mountain top b) 1.5×10^{-5} radians **4** 2.9×10^{-7} m **5** 8.3×10^{10} km **6** 63 pc **7** the speed with which a galaxy recedes is proportional to its distance/$t = d/v$

 If you got them all right, skip to page 75

Astrophysics

Improve your knowledge

1 Stars are formed from interstellar clouds of gas and dust. The gas comprises mainly hydrogen with some helium and trace amounts of lithium. The density of the cloud will be non-uniform and star formation commences when the cloud starts to collapse around a region of high density.

Key points from
AS in a Week
Furrther waves
page 53

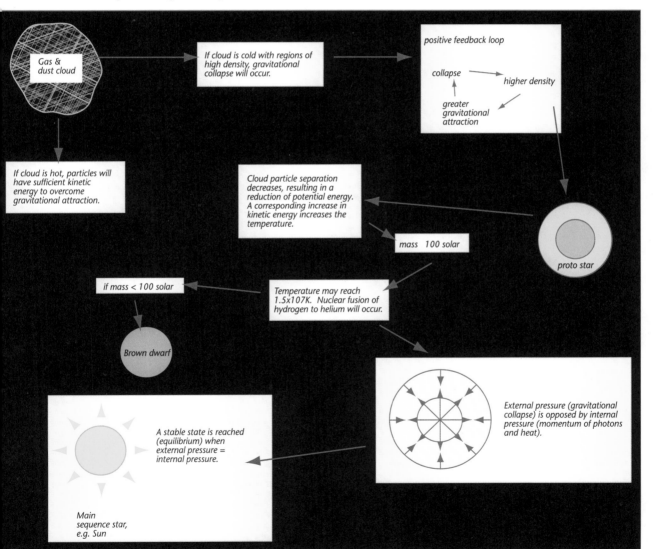

Gas & dust cloud

If cloud is cold with regions of high density, gravitational collapse will occur.

positive feedback loop

collapse → higher density → greater gravitational attraction → collapse

If cloud is hot, particles will have sufficient kinetic energy to overcome gravitational attraction.

Cloud particle separation decreases, resulting in a reduction of potential energy. A corresponding increase in kinetic energy increases the temperature.

mass 100 solar

proto star

if mass < 100 solar

Temperature may reach 1.5x107K. Nuclear fusion of hydrogen to helium will occur.

Brown dwarf

External pressure (gravitational collapse) is opposed by internal pressure (momentum of photons and heat).

A stable state is reached (equilibrium) when external pressure = internal pressure.

Main sequence star, e.g. Sun

2 The future of a main sequence star is dependent upon its mass. The mass will determine the nature of the subsequent bodies formed and the speed of evolution.

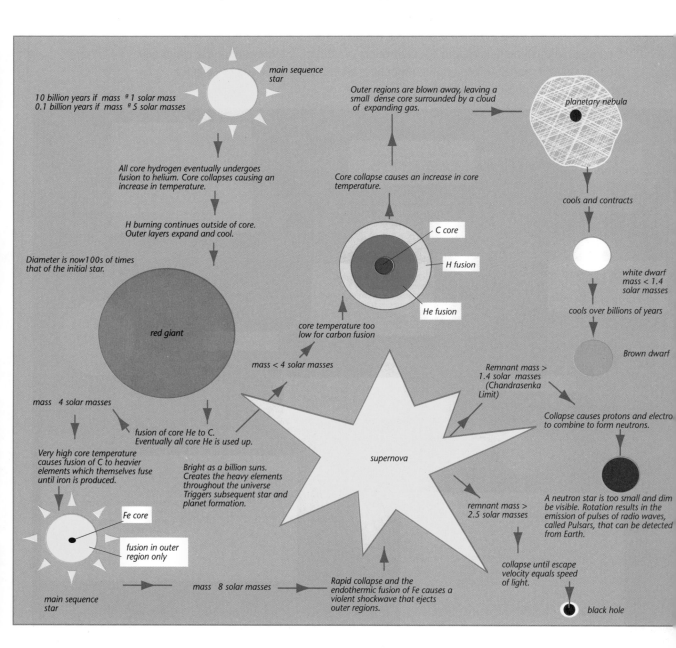

10 billion years if mass ª 1 solar mass
0.1 billion years if mass ª 5 solar masses

main sequence
star

Outer regions are blown away, leaving a
small dense core surrounded by a cloud
of expanding gas.

planetary nebula

All core hydrogen eventually undergoes
fusion to helium. Core collapses causing an
increase in temperature.

Core collapse causes an increase in core
temperature.

cools and contracts

H burning continues outside of core.
Outer layers expand and cool.

C core

H fusion

Diameter is now100s of times
that of the initial star.

He fusion

white dwarf
mass < 1.4
solar masses

red giant

core temperature too
low for carbon fusion

cools over billions of years

mass < 4 solar masses

Brown dwarf

mass 4 solar masses

Remnant mass >
1.4 solar masses
(Chandrasenka
Limit)

fusion of core He to C.
Eventually all core He is used up.

supernova

Collapse causes protons and electro
to combine to form neutrons.

Very high core temperature
causes fusion of C to heavier
elements which themselves fuse
until iron is produced.

Bright as a billion suns.
Creates the heavy elements
throughout the universe
Triggers subsequent star and
planet formation.

A neutron star is too small and dim
be visible. Rotation results in the
emission of pulses of radio waves,
called Pulsars, that can be detected
from Earth.

remnant mass >
2.5 solar masses

Fe core

fusion in outer
region only

collapse until escape
velocity equals speed
of light.

main sequence
star

mass 8 solar masses

Rapid collapse and the
endothermic fusion of Fe causes a
violent shockwave that ejects
outer regions.

black hole

Astrophysics

 We see stars in the sky by observing their emitted electromagnetic radiation and planets by their reflected sunlight. Early observations were made by the naked eye and optical telescopes. In modern astronomy, information is gained by detecting and analysing radiation across the electromagnetic spectrum.

Not all wavelengths of electromagnetic radiation can travel to the Earth's surface, as the atmosphere absorbs them. X-rays and gamma rays are heavily absorbed with negligible amounts passing through and ultraviolet light is strongly absorbed by ozone. Telescopes that detect ultraviolet, X-ray or gamma sources have to be placed above the atmosphere.

The atmosphere is transparent to two bands of electromagnetic wavelengths: visible light with some infrared and ultraviolet, and radio waves between 10 cm and 100 m.

Even when detecting signals within these 'optical windows' there are problems with observation by Earth-based telescopes.

- Earth-based light sources can make dim stars invisible.

- Varying thermal currents cause inconsistent refraction.

- Electrical appliances can add interference to radio astronomy signals.

- Light is scattered and absorbed by dust and molecules in the atmosphere.

These difficulties can be limited by placing telescopes at high altitudes, e.g. on high mountains, and on satellites and space probes.

Refracting telescope

This comprises two lenses: the objective lens of very long focal length and the eyepiece lens of short focal length. A distance exactly equal to the sum of their focal lengths separates the lenses.

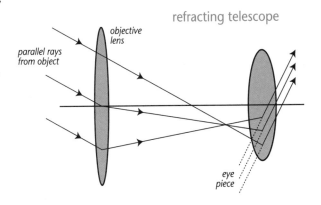

refracting telescope

$$\text{Magnifying power} = \frac{\text{focal length objective lens}}{\text{focal length of eyepiece lens}}$$

Reflecting telescopes have a number of advantages over refracting telescopes:

- It is easier to support very large mirrors than lenses, so very dim and distant objects can be observed in detail.

- Mirrors do not suffer from chromatic aberration (the spectral separation of light colours).

Astrophysics

- Mirrors do not suffer from spherical aberration (rays focusing at slightly different positions due to the curvature of the lens).

However, there are disadvantages:

- The mirrors need to be periodically re-silvered.

- The dimensions of the mirror will change due to temperature fluctuations.

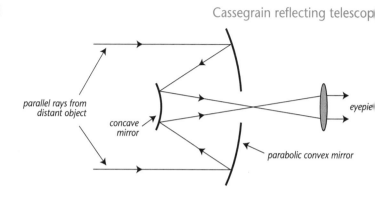

parallel rays from distant object

concave mirror

parabolic convex mirror

eyepiece

The resolving power of a telescope is a measure of its ability to distinguish between two separate objects. When light from a star enters the circular aperture of a telescope diffraction occurs, giving a bright central disc surrounded by concentric rings. The rings and the discs may overlap.

Rayleigh's criterion states that the stars are just resolved when the central ring of one image falls on the first dark ring of the other.

The minimum angular separation for two stars to be resolved is given by:

$$\Delta\theta_{min} = \frac{1.22\lambda}{D}$$

$$\text{Resolving power} = \frac{1}{\Delta\theta_{min}}$$

$\Delta\theta$ = angular separation of stars in radians
λ = wavelength of light
D = diameter of objective lens in m
The larger the objective lens, the greater its resolving power.

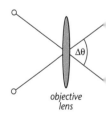

objective lens

The Radio Telescope

To achieve satisfactory resolution when making observation using radio waves ($\lambda = 1\,m$ to $10^5\,m$) a very large-diameter receiver dish is required. Spherical aberration is a problem and to minimise this radio telescope dishes are parabolic.

Radio waves falling upon the dish are reflected to a wave-guide positioned at the principal focus. From there they are amplified by a factor of up to 1000 before passing to the detector and display unit. The intensity of radio signals is generally very low and so large arrays of radio telescopes are linked together and operate as a single very large telescope. To limit problems created by wind, radio telescope dishes are often made from wire mesh.

Astrophysics

4 The luminosity, L, of a star gives the total power emitted by the star. The higher the temperature of a star, the greater its luminosity. Star luminosity can be determined from a knowledge of the surface temperature using Stefan's law:

$$L = 4\pi R^2 \sigma T^4$$

T = surface temperature/K
R = Radius of star/m
σ = Stefan's constant = $5.67 \times 10^{-8} Wm^{-2}K^{-4}$

The surface temperature of the star can be determined if the wavelength at which the star emits most of its power (emissive power wavelength λ_{max}) is known. Diffraction gratings can be used to separate the electromagnetic radiation received from the star into its component wavelengths and therefore λ_{max} can be established. The greater λ_{max}, the lower the temperature of the star. Wein's law gives:

$$\lambda_{max} T = constant = 2.898 \times 10^{-3} Km$$

This assumes that stars are black bodies, i.e. perfect absorbers and emitters of radiation. The surface temperatures of stars range from almost 0 K to 10^7 K.

The power that falls upon the Earth, per m^2, is called intensity and is given by:

$$Intensity = \frac{L}{4\pi d^2}$$

d = distance of star/m

5 When considering astronomical distances the term light year is often used. This is the distance that light will travel in one year. One light year = $9.4650 \times 10^{15} m$

We can determine the distance of nearby stars using parallax. This relies upon the fact that when a star is observed from Earth its position in the sky, when compared to a fixed background of distant stars, depends upon the Earth's position in its annual orbit of the Sun.

θ, the difference in the direction of the star when observations are made six months apart, is measured, in radians, at Earth. The parallax angle, p, is given by

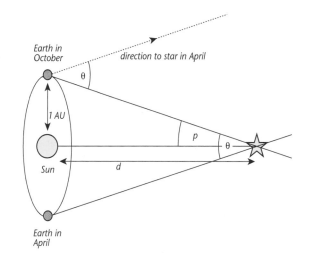

Earth in
October

direction to star in April

θ

1 AU

Sun

d

p

θ

Earth in
April

fixed-position distant
stars

θ/2 and 1 Au is the average distance between the Sun and the Earth (1.496×10^{11} m). The distance to the star, d, is given by:

$$d = \frac{1}{p}$$

p in seconds of a[r]

A distance of one parsec (pc) is defined as the distance when the parallax angle is one second of arc i.e. $\frac{1}{3600°}$.

One parsec = 3.2 light years = 3×10^{16} m.

Parallax angles are very small, and the further away a star is the smaller they become. Currently the smallest measurements that can be made on Earth are about 0.02 seconds of arc, which allow measurements of less than 7000 stars.

Cepheid variables are stars whose luminosities vary periodically. The distances, and hence luminosities, of nearby Cepheid variables can be established and it is found that there is a fixed relationship between the period of fluctuation and distance. Therefore measuring the period of distant stars allows their luminosities to be found and comparing this to the measured intensity recorded earth allows their distance to be calculated from:

$$d = \sqrt{\frac{L}{4\pi I}}$$

6 An apparent magnitude (brightness) scale for stars was originally established by the Greeks and ranged from 1 to 6, where magnitude 1 was the brightest that could be seen with the naked eye and 6 the dimmest. Measurements of light intensity have shown that the ratio of brightness between a magnitude 1 and a magnitude 6 star is 100, and it follows that a difference in magnitude of 1 corresponds to an intensity ratio of 2.5. Accurate measurements of intensity have allowed the scale to be extended and many stars have negative magnitudes, such as the Sun (−26.7).

The usefulness of apparent magnitudes is limited to comparison of stars that are equidistant. Distant stars may have a much greater luminosity than the Sun but appear dimmer as they are further away. To allow stars of different distances to be compared, absolute magnitudes are used. Absolute magnitude is defined as the apparent magnitude that a star would have if it were placed at a distance of 10 pc. This is a property of the actual luminosity of the star and is independent of distance. Apparent magnitude, m, is related to absolute magnitude, M, by:

$$m - M = 5\log\frac{d}{10}$$

d is in parsec

Astrophysics

The Hertzsprung–Russell diagram, as shown, is a plot of the absolute magnitude of stars against temperature. The main sequence stars are contained within a diagonal band extending from the top left to bottom right. The stars in region A are relatively cool and bright, such as red giants. In region B the stars are relatively hot and dim as they are very small, such as white dwarfs. The evolution of the star can be plotted as a track on the Hertzsprung–Russell diagram as shown.

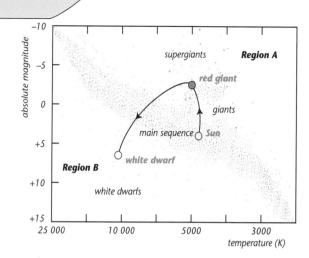

7 When the separation between a wave emitter and observer decreases, the wave received will have an increased frequency and corresponding decreased wavelength. This is called the Doppler effect:

$$\frac{\Delta f}{f} = \frac{v}{c}$$

Δf = frequency shift
v = speed of emitter
f = original frequency
c = speed of wave

If the separation is increasing, the frequency will decrease in the same manner.

When observing electromagnetic radiation an increase in frequency is called a red shift and a decrease is called a blue shift. So by observing the shift in frequency of the electromagnetic radiation received from galaxies we can tell whether they are moving towards or away from us, and also their velocities relative to Earth. It is found that on average that the galaxies are all moving away from us (receding) i.e. they are all red-shifted. This is called the Hubble red shift.

Hubble's law states that the speed with which a galaxy recedes is proportional to its distance, i.e.:

$$v = H_0 d$$

H_0 is known as the Hubble constant

$$\frac{1}{H_0} = t = \text{age of universe}$$

This gives a value for the age of the universe of about 20 billion years. An estimate allowing for the deceleration of the galaxies gives a value of between 15 and 18 billion years.

Accepting that the universe is expanding, and always has been expanding, leads to the theory that originally all of the galaxies were in the same place. The Big Bang model states that the universe started from an explosion at a single point. Supporting evidence for this includes:

- Observed red shifts, i.e. an expanding universe.

- Cosmic microwave background radiation suggesting a universe average temperature of 2.728 K which is very close to that predicted to be the remnant heat of the very hot Big Bang.

- The observed abundances of helium, deuterium and lithium are in the ratios as predicted by the model.

- The temperature of distant galaxies is greater than those closer. This suggests that galaxies are cooling since the information received from distant galaxies originated from further back in time (takes a long time to reach us).

The fate of the universe depends on the value of its density, ρ, in relation to a certain critical density, ρ_c.

- If $\rho < \rho_c$, endless expansion (open or unbounded universe).

- If $\rho > \rho_c$, expansion will cease, followed by contraction i.e. 'Big Crunch' (closed or bound universe).

- If $\rho = \rho_c$, endless expansion at an ever-decreasing rate tending to a finite maximum (flat or marginally bounded universe).

The current belief is that the density of the universe is very close to that required for a flat universe:

$$\rho_c = \frac{3H_0^2}{8\pi G}$$

Astrophysics

Use your knowledge

1 Draw a simple Hertzsprung–Russell diagram and indicate on it the position of main sequence stars, red giants and white dwarfs.

2 A star is 20×10^{20} m from Earth and has a surface temperature of 5200 K. The measured intensity of the star at Earth is 5×10^{-6} Wm^{-2}. Calculate:
a) the luminosity of the star
b) the radius of the star.

Use Stefan's Law

Stefan's constant
$= 5.67 \times 10^{-8}$ Wm^{-2}K^{-4}

3 A star is observed to have a parallax of 0.06 seconds of arc.
a) Label this angle on an appropriate diagram, which should include the Earth, the star and the Sun.
b) Calculate the distance, in metres, from the Earth to the star.

$d = \frac{1}{p}$

4 There is a theory that suggests that the universe started with an explosion at a singularity.
a) Name this theory.
b) What evidence is there to support this theory?

5 A main sequence star can end its life as a black hole. List the intermediate stages in its evolution and state the mass requirements for each stage.

6 Outline the possible fates of the universe, stating the density conditions required for them to occur.

Medical Physics

Test your knowledge

1
a) State the minimum frequency of ultrasound.
b) What range of ultrasound frequencies are used for scanning applications?
c) Determine the percentages of ultrasound beam intensity reflected from the wall of an abdomen which is scanned with and without a coupling medium.
$Z_{air} = 0.43 \times 10^3 \, kgm^2s^{-1}$
$Z_{tissue} = 1630 \times 10^3 \, kgm^2s^{-1}$
$Z_{gel} = 1500 \times 10^3 \, kgm^2s^{-1}$

2
a) Describe the function of the swept gain generator in the simple A-scope.
b) When an ultrasonic Doppler probe is placed at angle of 30° to an artery, a frequency shift of 3 kHz is detected. If the original frequency of the ultrasound is 4 MHz and the ultrasound travels at 1500 ms^{-1}, calculate the speed of the blood flow.

3 X-rays are produced by rapidly _____ high speed _____ . The mechanisms by which X-rays are produced are: _____ , which produces a _____ spectrum, and _____ , which produces a _____ spectrum.

4 What is the function of the lead grid when taking an X-ray photograph?

5 State three criteria that have to be satisfied in the selection of a radioisotope for medical imaging.

6 Describe how an image of the lungs could be gained using a suitable radioactive tracer.

Answers

1 a) 20kHz b) 1 to 15MHz c) with 0.17%/without 99.89% **2** a) Amplifies ultrasound signals in proportion to the distance travelled in the body. This ensures that the signal strength reveals the impedance of the media. b) 0.65ms^{-1} **3** decelerating/electrons/Bremsstrahlung/continuous/ionisation/discrete **4** Ensures that scattered photons do not reach the photographic film. **5** Biologically targeted, gamma emitter, sufficiently long half-life for investigation. **6** Radioactive xenon gas can be inhaled into the lungs and its emissions detected with a gamma camera.

 If you got them all right, skip to page 83

Medical Physics

40 minutes

Improve your knowledge

1 Ultrasound is a sound wave with a frequency greater than 20 kHz. Ultrasound waves reflect from the interface between media of different densities, such as bone and soft tissue. This allows them to be used for the non-invasive observation of internal organs. They are used in the frequency range 1 to 15 MHz.

Key points from AS in a Week

The nucleus and radioactivity
page 78

Applying an alternating potential difference across a piezoelectric crystal, such as quartz, creates ultrasound waves. At appropriate frequencies the crystal will oscillate at its resonant frequency and emit an ultrasound wave.

The speed of ultrasound depends upon the medium through which it travels, e.g. $1500 \, ms^{-1}$ in soft tissue and $330 \, ms^{-1}$ in air. The acoustic impedance, Z, of a material is given by:

$$Z = \rho c$$

Z = acoustic impedance/$kg m^{-2} s^{-1}$
ρ = density/$kg m^{-3}$
c = wave speed/ms^{-1}

When the ultrasound reaches an interface between two media of different acoustic impedance, a proportion of the incoming beam will be reflected. The ratio of the reflected beam to the incident beam is called the intensity reflection coefficient, α, and the greater the difference between acoustic impedance the greater the value of α.

$$\alpha = \frac{I_r}{I_i} = \frac{\left(Z_1 - Z_2\right)^2}{\left(Z_1 + Z_2\right)^2}$$

When taking a scan, perhaps through the wall of the abdomen, reflection due to the significant difference in acoustic impedance at the air–skin boundary has to be minimised. A coupling medium is applied, such as a gel, which displaces the air and has a Z-value close to that of skin.

2 When a short pulse of ultrasound is reflected from an internal boundary, e.g. a heart wall, its 'echo' can be detected. The time delay between emitting the pulse and detecting the echo can be measured and used to calculate the depth of the organ:

$$d = \frac{ct}{2}$$

d = depth
c = ultrasound speed
t = echo delay

In an A-scan (amplitude) the intensity of the reflected wave is plotted against time. The features appear as spikes. This is used for scanning the eye. For a B-scan (brightness), the display comprises spots whose brightness gives a measure of the intensity of the reflected beam.

A-scan apparatus

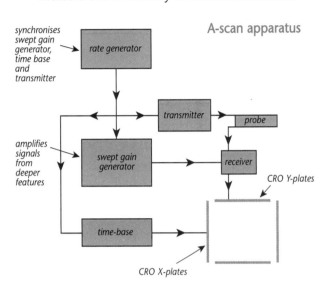

synchronises swept gain generator, time base and transmitter

amplifies signals from deeper features

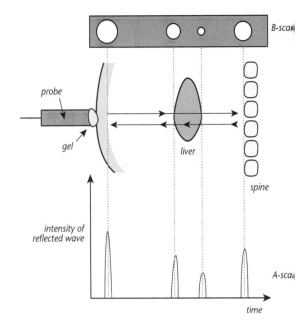

probe

gel

liver

spine

intensity of reflected wave

B-scan

A-scan

time

In a time-position scan (M-scan) the spots of a B-scan are recorded over regular time intervals. These are recorded on a chart, which plots depth (spot positions) against time. Periodic movement within the body can be charted, e.g. heart valves.

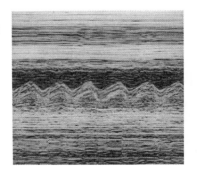

A two-dimensional B-scan produces an image of a cross-section through the body. The probe is moved across the relevant body part and its orientation varied. The orientation and location of the probe is detected with position sensors, which position the B-scan spot on the display correspondingly by applying an appropriate potential to the deflecting plates of the CRO. Each of these form a pixel, and the pixels combine to form an image. Successively scanned images can be displayed in rapid succession to form a real time moving image of internal organs. This leads to more straightforward analysis but sacrifices image quality.

High-frequency ultrasound improves resolution but is attenuated (loses energy) due to absorption and scattering. As a compromise it is found that scanning wavelength, λ, is given by:

$$\lambda = \frac{200}{d}$$

d = scan dept

When ultrasound is reflected off a moving surface its frequency is increased due to the Doppler effect. The frequency shift, Δf, is given by:

$$\Delta f = \frac{2fv\cos\phi}{c}$$

f = original frequency
v = speed of reflecting surface
c = speed of ultrasound
ϕ = angle between probe and motion

The speed of blood flow or the monitoring of foetal heart valve movement could be achieved by detection of the frequency shift. The transmitted and received frequencies are filtered and the frequency shift is amplified. This is in the audible range so it can be monitored by an operator with earphones and presented graphically.

There are no dangerous side-effects in the normal use of ultrasound. However, at excessively high beam powers and frequencies, damage can occur due to heating and pressure effects. These effects can be used therapeutically, e.g. the heating of deep-lying tissue for pain relief in arthritic joints and the fragmentation of gallstones.

3 X-rays are used in medicine for diagnosis (e.g. detection of broken bones) and therapy (e.g. treatment of tumours). They are produced by rapidly decelerating high-speed electrons by collision with a high-density target, such as tungsten. X-rays are produced by two mechanisms; Bremsstrahlung, which produces X-rays with photons of a continuous range of energies/frequencies (continuous spectrum); and ionisation, which produces photons with a limited number of specific energies (discrete spectrum).

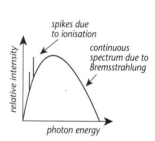

The high-speed electrons are produced by passing a large current (tube current) through a filament, which are then accelerated towards the target by the application of a potential difference between the target and the filament. The intensity of the X-ray beam is given by:

intensity $\propto IV^2$

If the tube PD is increased, the:

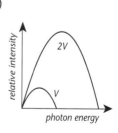

- peak height will increase in proportion to V^2

- maximum photon energy will increase in proportion to V

- peak position will shift to higher photon energy

- minimum photon energy remains at zero.

If the tube current is increased, the:

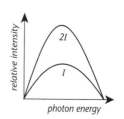

- maximum energy of the photons is unchanged

- minimum energy of the photons is unchanged
- peak height increases in proportion to the current
- peak position remains unchanged.

The photons of a monochromatic or homogeneous beam all have the same frequency/energy. In a heterogeneous beam the photons have a range of energies/frequencies.

When a beam of X-rays pass through matter, a constant fraction of its energy is lost (attenuation) per unit distance travelled.

$$-\frac{\delta I}{I} = \mu \delta x \quad \text{or} \quad I = I_0 e^{-\mu x}$$

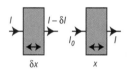

μ is the total linear attenuation coefficient and is dependent upon photon frequency.

The half-value thickness, $x_{1/2}$, is the distance that the beam travels before its intensity is attenuated to half of its original value:

$$x_{1/2} = \frac{\ln 2}{\mu}$$

The harder a beam, the greater its penetrating power. When an X-ray beam passes through body matter, low-energy photons are absorbed. These can cause damage to tissue, by ionisation, and do not contribute to the radiograph image. Passing the beam through a few millimetres of aluminium before it enters the body removes the low-energy photons. This is called filtering and makes the beam harder while increasing its quality by reducing the range of photon energies.

 When X-rays are used for diagnosis the degree of attenuation must vary significantly between different kinds of matter, i.e. skin soft tissue and bone. 30 keV is found to be the optimum photon energy.

The lead grid (see diagram) ensures that scattered photons do not reach the photographic film. The image-intensifying screens are made from zinc sulphide and amplify the effect of the X-rays; lower doses are required to achieve acceptable picture quality.

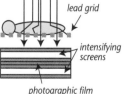

X-rays can be used to treat tumours as they destroy malignant cells. Up to 5 MeV beams are used, as at this energy attenuation is independent of proton number.

Medical Physics

To achieve a high concentration of X-rays at the target site, beams are aimed at the tumour from different directions, intersecting at the tumour.

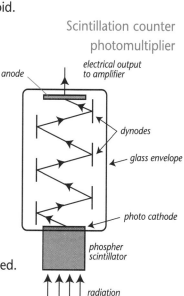

Emissions from radioisotopes can be used for diagnosis (tracers and imaging) and therapeutically (treatment of cancer).

In diagnosis a gamma emitter is introduced into the body and its emission monitored externally. The radioisotope should fulfil three criteria:

- be biologically targeted
- be a gamma emitter (exclusively is preferable)
- have a sufficiently long half-life for investigation.

The effective half-life of a radioisotope within the body will be lower than that determined by radioactive decay alone. The body will remove and disperse the isotope causing a biological half-life, given by:

$$\frac{1}{T_E} = \frac{1}{T_B} + \frac{1}{T_R}$$

T_E = effective half-life
T_B = biological half-life
T_R = radioactive half-life

5 To investigate the activity of the thyroid gland, iodine-131 is ingested and eventually accumulates in the thyroid gland. A collimated scintillation counter is used (see diagram) to monitor count rate and this is compared with the rate expected from a thyroid that functions normally. If the count rate decreases more rapidly than expected, the thyroid is overactive. A less rapid decrease indicates an underactive thyroid.

Action of the scintillation counter:

- Radiation falls on the phosphor scintillator, which emits light.
- Light falls on the photocathode causing it to emit electrons.
- The electrons are accelerated along the tube by the potential differences between the dynodes.
- Each time an electron strikes a dynode it emits 4 electrons, on average.
- An electron cascade causes a signal magnification of up to 10^8.
- The electrical signal gives a measure of the activity of the radioactive sample.

A gamma camera can be used to provide an image of a targeted organ. Radioactive xenon gas can be inhaled into the lungs and its emissions detected.

Scintillation counter
photomultiplier

The collimator only allows rays that are perpendicular to the crystal to pass (compare with lead grid in X-rays section). The sodium iodide crystal acts as a scintillator, i.e. emits light photons when irradiated by gamma rays. An array of between 20 and 70 photomultiplier tubes amplify the signal and allow the precise determination of the location of the emitter. A dot (pixel) is plotted in a corresponding position on the CRO screen. Approximately 10 million pixels combine to form an image.

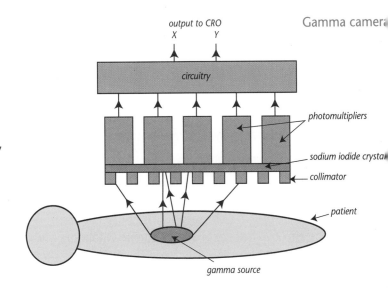

Gamma camera

output to CRO
X   Y

circuitry

photomultipliers

sodium iodide crystal

collimator

patient

gamma source

Medical Physics

Use your knowledge

1

a) The block diagram represents a simple ultrasound A-scope. Add labels to boxes in the diagram.

b) The A-scan peaks shown represent reflections from the outer surface and mid-line of the brain. If the ultrasound travels at $1500\,ms^{-1}$ in brain matter, determine the width of a brain hemisphere.

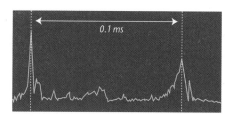

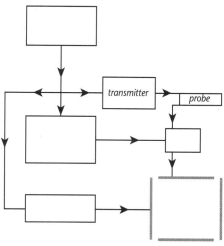

use $I = I_0 e^{-\mu x}$

2

a) Sketch labelled spectra, on the same axes, of X-rays obtained with a tube potential difference of $50\,kV$ and $80\,kV$ respectively.

b) Why, and how, are X-ray beams filtered before being used for diagnosis?

c) An X-ray beam of intensity I_0 passes through $5\,mm$ of a material and its intensity is reduced to $I_0/5$. Calculate:

   i) the total linear attenuation coefficient

   ii) the half-value thickness.

3

A radioactive tracer has a radioactive half-life of 2 hours and in an investigation of a diseased organ a measured effective half-life of 1.2 hours. It is known that for a healthy organ the biological half-life should be 2 hours. Comment upon the rate of activity of the diseased organ.

Materials

Test your knowledge

1. The graph shows how the potential energy of a pair of particles depends on their separation.

   a) Determine the separation of the particles when the resultant force between them is zero. What is this separation called?

   b) Determine the bond energy for these particles at 0 K.

   c) The pair of atoms is given 6.5×10^{-21} J of kinetic energy. Use the graph to find their new average separation. Comment on your result.

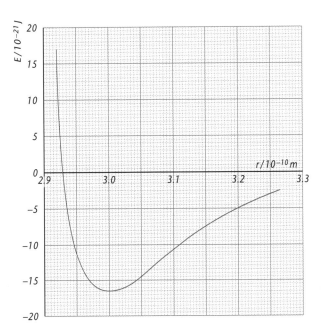

2. A structure that has long-range order is termed _____ . If there is an extra or missing plane of atoms in the structure, there is an edge _____ . The plane along which this defect moves is termed the _____ plane.

3. Match the following terms with the correct definition:

Fatigue	a) Repeated stress cycles resulting in plastic deformation
Pinning	b) A metallic material formed by chemically combining two or more elements
Annealing	c) Failure below the ultimate tensile stress (UTS) due to crack growth/repeated stress cycles
Creep	d) Heating a metal and allow it to cool slowly
Work hardening	e) Plastic deformation occurring when a constant stress is applied for a long time
Alloy	f) Inhibition of dislocation movement

Answers

 If you got them all right, skip to page 88

30 minutes

Improve your knowledge

 1 Material structure

Atoms in solids and molecules are linked together by these electrical forces:

Key points from
AS in a Week

Solids   page 64

- An attractive electric force, between the positive nucleus and the electron shells. This force is long range and negative as it tends to cause a decrease in separation.

- A repulsive electric force, between the outer electron shells on the atoms. This force only acts over a very short range and is positive as it tends to cause an increase in separation.

- These forces combine to produce a resultant force, which varies with separation and is used to explain the presence of inter-particle bonds.

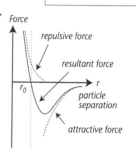

When the attractive force balances the repulsive force, there is no resultant force and the atoms are at their equilibrium separation, r_0. If the particles are disturbed from this equilibrium separation, the resultant force acts to restore the particles to the equilibrium separation.

A graph representing how the potential energy in the bonds varies with separation is also shown for the two particles. The energy at a certain separation, r, is equal to the area under the force–distance graph from that separation to infinite separation. The particles are most stable at the equilibrium separation. At this point the potential energy is at its lowest, as the particles require the greatest energy to separate them to infinity. This energy is the bond energy (E_0).

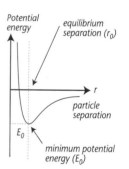

The microscopic (small-scale) model can be used to predict macroscopic (large scale) properties of solids. Two specific examples follow:

- Hooke's law. The resultant force on the particles for separations close to their equilibrium separation is approximately a straight line graph – i.e. the extension or compression from equilibrium is proportional to the applied force.

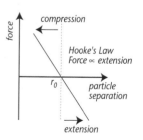

- Thermal expansion If the particles are at absolute zero (0 K), the particles have no translational kinetic energy and are at rest at their equilibrium separation (r_0). The diagram magnifies part of the energy–separation graph about r_0. If the atoms are at a higher temperature, they have kinetic energy and oscillate about the base of the potential energy well. The average separation (indicated by '×' on the graph) is greater than the equilibrium separation, as the energy graph is asymmetrical – the atoms oscillate further outwards (r_{max}) than

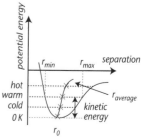

inwards (r_{min}). This effect becomes bigger at higher temperatures, so the average separation increases with temperature (indicated as $r_{average}$ on the graph). This is thermal expansion.

2 Defects in crystals

A semi-crystalline material, such as a metal, has large regions of atoms stacked in an ordered fashion. However, there are irregularities that affect the materials' properties – e.g. their strength is reduced considerably.

An edge dislocation is a disruption to the regular stacking sequence in a crystal as an extra plane of atoms has been added or is missing. This creates a distortion to the lattice. The bonds are deformed and so are weakened (see the above graph of potential energy against separation).

Any stress applied to the crystal will result in these weak bonds breaking, so effectively allowing the dislocation to move through the crystal. The plane along which it moves is called the slip plane. The diagrams show the motion of a dislocation under the action of stress. As bonds have been broken, this is plastic deformation. Because the bonds are weak, plastic deformation occurs at lower stresses than predicted.

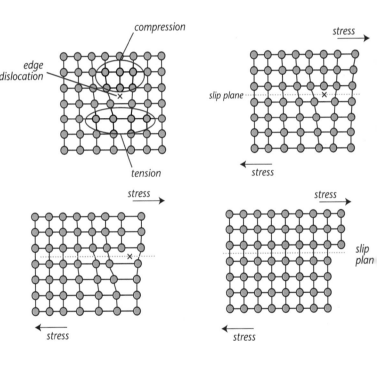

3 Tailoring material properties

By designing or treating materials, the dislocations can either be allowed or prevented from moving. This has marked effects on the macroscopic properties of the materials (e.g. strength, flexibility, etc.). The following flow diagram outlines the main effects.

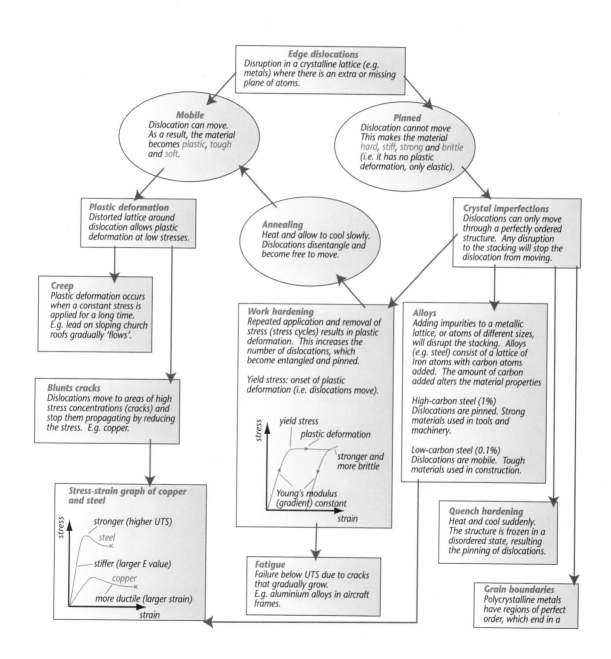

Edge dislocations
Disruption in a crystalline lattice (e.g. metals) where there is an extra or missing plane of atoms.

Mobile
Dislocation can move.
As a result, the material becomes *plastic*, *tough* and *soft*.

Pinned
Dislocation cannot move
This makes the material *hard*, *stiff*, *strong* and *brittle* (i.e. it has no plastic deformation, only elastic).

Plastic deformation
Distorted lattice around dislocation allows plastic deformation at low stresses.

Annealing
Heat and allow to cool slowly.
Dislocations disentangle and become free to move.

Crystal imperfections
Dislocations can only move through a perfectly ordered structure. Any disruption to the stacking will stop the dislocation from moving.

Creep
Plastic deformation occurs when a constant stress is applied for a long time.
E.g. lead on sloping church roofs gradually 'flows'.

Work hardening
Repeated application and removal of stress (stress cycles) results in plastic deformation. This increases the number of dislocations, which become entangled and pinned.

Yield stress: onset of plastic deformation (i.e. dislocations move).

Alloys
Adding impurities to a metallic lattice, or atoms of different sizes, will disrupt the stacking. Alloys (e.g. steel) consist of a lattice of Iron atoms with carbon atoms added. The amount of carbon added alters the material properties

High-carbon steel (1%)
Dislocations are pinned. Strong materials used in tools and machinery.

Low-carbon steel (0.1%)
Dislocations are mobile. Tough materials used in construction.

Blunts cracks
Dislocations move to areas of high stress concentrations (cracks) and stop them propagating by reducing the stress. E.g. copper.

Stress-strain graph of copper and steel

stronger (higher UTS)
steel
stiffer (larger E value)
copper
more ductile (larger strain)

Fatigue
Failure below UTS due to cracks that gradually grow.
E.g. aluminium alloys in aircraft frames.

Quench hardening
Heat and cool suddenly.
The structure is frozen in a disordered state, resulting the pinning of dislocations.

Grain boundaries
Polycrystalline metals have regions of perfect order, which end in a

Materials

Use your knowledge

1 The diagram shows how the inter-particle force varies with their separation.

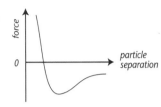

a) Explain why the graph has this shape and define the equilibrium separation.

b) Sketch the corresponding potential energy–separation graph.

c) Using the graphs, explain the macroscopic i) tensile stress–strain behaviour at small strains, and ii) why metals expand on heating.

2 a) Explain what is meant by an *edge dislocation*. Include a diagram in your answer.

b) Using diagrams, explain how the dislocation is able to move through a crystal. Include a definition of the *slip plane* in your answer.

3 Explain how a metal may fail due to *fatigue* after undergoing repeated stress cycles. Give an example where this effect is important.

4 a) Describe an *alloy* in terms of its microstructure.

b) Draw the typical stress–strain graphs for an alloy and a polycrystalline metal, using the same set of axes.

Synoptic

20 minutes

Test your knowledge

1 a) The extension of a spring for a varying force is described by _____ law, up to the limit of _____ ($F = kx$). Capacitance is defined as the ability to store _____ per volt ($Q = CV$).

b) Define the quantities in the capacitor equation that are analogous to those in the spring equation $F = kx$.

c) i) Describe two ways in which electrical and gravitational fields are similar.
   ii) Describe two ways in which they are different.

2 a) If a charged particle is injected into an electric field, travelling along the field direction, its speed _____ without changing its direction of _____ . The change in kinetic energy comes from the _____ energy of the electric field.

hot filament emitting electrons

accelerating voltage (V)

b) If a particle of mass m is accelerated from rest by a potential V, show that its resulting velocity is given by:

$$v = \sqrt{\frac{2qV}{m}}$$

cylindrical anode

c) A beam of electrons is accelerated from rest to a speed of $3.0 \times 10^6 \text{ms}^{-1}$. It then passes through a perpendicular electric field, as shown in the diagram. If the plate potential is 5.0V and their separation is 3.0cm, and the plates 8.4cm long, calculate:

0V　　*+5V*

electron path

   i) the time taken to travel through the plates
   ii) field strength between the plates
   iii) the horizontal acceleration of the electrons
   iv) the horizontal deflection of the electrons as they leave the electric field (to the nearest centimetre).

Electron mass = 9.1×10^{-31} kg

Electron charge = 1.6×10^{-19} C

Answers

1 a) Hooke's/proportionality/charge b) $F \rightarrow V$, $k \rightarrow 1/C$, $x \rightarrow Q$ c) i), ii) see table in 'Improve your knowledge' 2 a) changes/travel/potential b) potential energy → kinetic energy; $qV = \frac{1}{2} mv^2$; $v = \sqrt{(2qV/m)}$ c) i) $t =$ distance/speed, $t = 2.8 \times 10^{-8}$ s ii) $E = V/d = 167$ NC^{-1} iii) $a = Eq/m = 2.9 \times 10^{13}$ ms^{-2} iv) $s = ut + 0.5at^2 = 0.012$m = 1.2 cm

 If you got them all right, skip to page 94

Improve your knowledge

This paper will draw together your understanding of different areas of physics. There are two main aspects to this, each of which is outlined in turn:

Key points from AS in a Week	
Solids	page 65

- Analogies: Comparing the similarities between different branches of physics.

- Synthesis: Applications or unfamiliar situations that require a knowledge of a variety of physical principles.

You will need to refer to other chapters in this book, as well as those in AS Physics in a Week for details about the topics discussed.

In addition there may be a comprehension and/or data handling question in your paper.

1 Analogies in physics

Comparison of Springs and Capacitors

The behaviour of springs, up to the limit of proportionality, is defined by Hooke's Law, $F = kx$. Capacitors are defined by their capacitance, $C = Q/V$.

Sprin

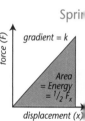

The analogy between these situations stems from the similarity of the spring stiffness (k) to the ability of a capacitor to store charge, the capacitance (C). These are summarised in the table below.

Capaci

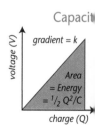

Property	Spring	Capacitor
Constant	k (spring constant)	1/C (capacitance)
Driving quantity	F (force)	V (voltage)
Responsive quantity	x (displacement)	Q (charge)
Defining equation	F = kx	V = (1/C) Q
Energy	$\frac{1}{2} Fx = \frac{1}{2} kx^2$	$\frac{1}{2} VQ = \frac{1}{2} (1/C) Q^2$

Comparison of Electric and Gravitational Fields

Property	Gravity	Electric
Force & field strength	Radial and $1/r^2$ field	
Force	Product of two 'field quantities' (either mass or charge)	
Force direction	Along field lines	
Motion of a charged particle when travelling along the field direction	Constant acceleration	
Motion of a charged particle when travelling at 90° to the field direction	Projectile motion in 2D: constant speed in the initial direction of travel and constant acceleration along field lines (at 90° to initial direction of travel)	
DIFFERENCES		
Ability to shield the field	No – only one type of mass	Yes – two types of charge
Size of force	Different, as different 'constants' (G and $1/4\,\pi\varepsilon_0$)	
What it acts on	Mass	Charge

Capacitors and Nuclear Decay

Property	Capacitor decay	Nuclear decay
Decay Quantity	Charge stored (Q)	Number of radioactive nuclei (N)
Decay constant	$1/\tau$ where τ is the time constant (RC)	λ decay constant = probability that any one nucleus decays in a second (s^{-1})
Relationship between decay constant and half-life	$(1/\tau)\,T_{1/2} = \ln 2$	$\lambda T_{1/2} = \ln 2$
Decay equation	$Q = Q_0\,e^{-t/t}$	$N = N_0\,e^{-\lambda t}$

Property	Capacitor decay	Nuclear decay
Gradient (rate of change of the decay quantity)	$\dfrac{dQ}{dt} = I$ Current = rate of flow of charge	$\dfrac{dN}{dt} = A = -\lambda N$ Activity = number of nuclei decaying per second
Variation of gradient with time	$I = I_0\,e^{-t/t}$ Exponential decay	$A = A_0\,e^{-\lambda t}$ Exponential decay

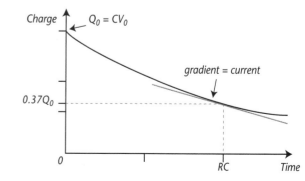

Synoptic

Synthesis of Physics

2 There are a wide variety of applications combining moving particles, gravitational, electric and magnetic fields, circular motion, projectile motion, Newton's laws, particle accelerators and detectors. These include:

1) Motion of charged particles in uniform electric fields

A charged particle is accelerated across a uniform electric field, just as a mass will accelerate if dropped in a gravitational field. Potential energy is converted into kinetic energy: $qV = \frac{1}{2}mv^2$.

These moving charged particles can then be introduced to a uniform electric field at right angles (90°) to their motion. Just as in projectile problems, where gravity acts downwards on a horizontally projected object, the charged particle is deflected, following a parabolic path. The constant electrical force, F, is towards the oppositely charged plate and is equal to Eq – where the field strength for a uniform field is $E = V/d$.

Applications of this include the cathode ray oscilloscope (**CRO**), linear particle accelerators (**LINAC**) and electron tubes, as used in television sets.

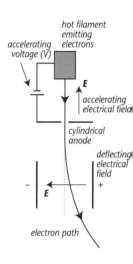

hot filament emitting electrons

accelerating voltage (V)

E accelerating electrical field

cylindrical anode

deflecting electrical field

E

electron path

q = charge (C
V = voltage (V
m = mass (kg
v = speed (ms⁻
d = plate separation (m

2) Motion of charged particles in magnetic fields

Since the magnetic force acts at right angles to the field direction and the current (Fleming's LHR), a circular motion results when a charge moves perpendicular to a magnetic flux density. NB conventional current is opposite to electron (negative charge) motion. Speed is constant as no work is done by the magnetic force (as compared to an electrical force which does work).

$$Bqv = mv^2/r$$

magnetic force = centripetal force

$$r = mv/qB$$

B = Magnetic flux density (
r = radius of orbit (m

Thus we can determine the radius of circular motion of a charge in a field of flux density B if we know the charge to mass ratio q/m.

This is used in mass spectrometers, where particles with the same velocity, but different q/m ratios are separated by having different radii. In cloud chambers, ionising radioactivity is detected as the particles condense water out of the saturated air, revealing its path.

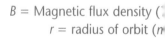

Cloud chamber: *the ionising effect of the particle condenses water out of the saturated air, revealing its path.*

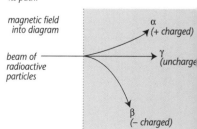

magnetic field into diagram

α (+ charged)

beam of radioactive particles

γ (uncharge

β (– charged)

3) Motion of charged particles in electric and magnetic fields

If a charged particle passes through an electric and magnetic field which are at 90° to each other as well as the direction of travel of the particle, it will only continue to travel in a straight path with constant speed if there is no resultant force acting on it (Newton's First Law). Therefore the Magnetic (F_B) and electric (F_E) forces must balance:

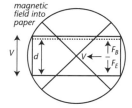

magnetic field into paper

$$F_B = F_E$$

$$Bqv = Eq \qquad \text{where } E = V/d \text{ for a uniform } E \text{ field}$$

$$v = E/B$$

Applications of this principle include:

Velocity selector: as the speed is independent of charge, this can be used to select particles travelling at the given speed (i.e. energy), irrespective of their charge or mass.

Hall probe: uses the size of electric field (actually the voltage) created as a measure of the magnetic flux density. $V_{Hall} = Bvd$

Determination of the e/m ratio for an electron

A different combination of the electric and magnetic fields is used in the cyclotron, where the electric field used to accelerate the charged particle, rather than deflect it.

Energy sources

Another field of physics that allows for the combination of a diversity of physical principles is that of energy sources. e.g. thermocouple (thermal), solar cell (electrical), nuclear (nuclear), dynamo (magnetic and AC current).

Synoptic

Use your knowledge

1   When charged particles are introduced at 90° to a magnetic field, they travel in circular paths.

a)   Explain what provides the centripetal force.

b)   Explain why the particles move at constant speed.

c)   Show that the radius described by a charged particle is given by:

$$r = \frac{mv}{Bq}$$ where m is the particle mass, v its speed and q the charge.

d)   Complete the following table describing the relative charge and mass on several radioactive decay products.

	Charge (e)	Mass (u)
Neutron	0	1
Proton		
α particle		
β particle		
γ radiation		

e)   During a radioactive decay, α, β and γ radiation is given out as well as neutrons and protons. Using your answers to c) and d), identify the path taken by each decay product, assuming they travel at the same speed.

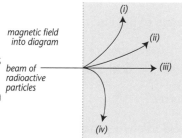

f)   If the particles were initially travelling along the magnetic field lines, how would their motion change, if at all?

g)   If the field were an electric field and the particles were initially travelling along the electric field lines, would they change speed or direction of travel?

Work done = forc x distance move in the direction c the force

Magnetic force = Bqv

Centripetal Forc = mv^2/r

Only charged particles are deflected.

Direction of deflection is give by Fleming's LHR

Radius $\propto m/q$

Magnetic force only acts when particles move a right angles to the magnetic field.

1 The diagrams below show a charged plate and a charged sphere arrangement.

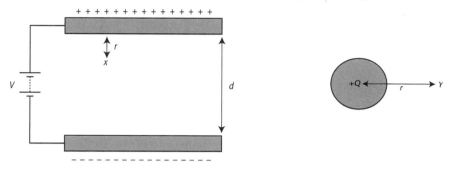

$r = 3\,cm \quad d = 18\,cm \quad V = 80\,V \quad Q = 2\,C \quad \varepsilon_0 = 8.9 \times 10^{-12}\,Fm^{-1}$

a) Add to each diagram at least four electric field lines (solid lines) and equipotential lines (dashed lines).

b) Calculate the value of:
   i) the electric field strength at X and Y
   ii) the electrical potential at X and Y
   iii) the force exerted on a $2\,C$ charge at both X and Y.

c) Describe qualitatively the nature of the motion of a positively charged particle released at both X and Y.

2 The diagram shows the path of an electron that travels through a uniform electric and magnetic field.

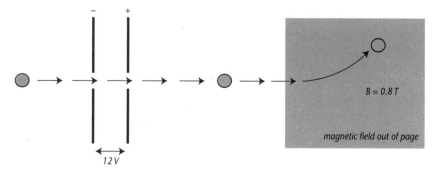

Taking the electronic charge to be $1.6 \times 10^{-19}\,C$, the electron mass to be $9.1 \times 10^{-31}\,kg$ and the speed of electron on entry to the electric field to be negligable, calculate the:

a) speed of the electron when it enters the magnetic field

b) radius of curvature of the electron's path as it moves through the magnetic field.

3 In the circuit shown, the capacitor is charged by closing switch A and then discharged by opening switch A and closing switch B.

Calculate:

a) the maximum charge stored on the capacitor
b) the energy stored on the capacitor when fully charged
c) the charge remaining on the capacitor 10 s after B is closed.

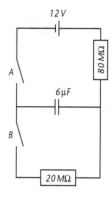

4 The diagram shows a simple pendulum and a mass–spring system oscillating with simple harmonic motion.

a) If both oscillate with the same period, 2 s, and amplitude, 3 cm, then calculate:
   i) the spring constant for the mass–spring system
   ii) the length of the pendulum.
b) If both systems were set oscillating in outer space, describe qualitatively how the periods of their motion may or may not change.

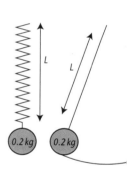

$(g = 9.8\,\text{ms}^{-2}$

5 a) Sketch a circuit diagram of a half-wave rectifier circuit.
b) Sketch graphically the potential difference variations with time of the input to and output from the half-wave rectifier circuit.
c) Explain how the half-wave rectified output can be smoothed.
d) In the same manner as part b), sketch the smoothed output.

6 A shower is designed to take cold water at 20 °C and heat it to 36 °C in a heater chamber before outputting it to the showerhead. The power of the shower is 4 kW.

a) Explain why the water reaches a constant temperature when operating.
b) Calculate the energy transferred to each m^3 of water that passes through the heater chamber.
c) What flow rate of water is required to achieve the desired temperature?

Density of water
$1.0 \times 10^3\,\text{kgm}^{-3}$

Specific heat
capacity of water
$=$
$4.2 \times 10^3\,\text{JK}^{-1}\text{kg}^{-1}$

Simple Harmonic Motion

1a) $250\,ms^{-2}$
b) $25.3\,m$
c) $79.5\,ms^{-1}$
d) $63.2\,kJ$
e) $46.7\,ms^{-1}$

2a) i) $\sqrt{0.02}\,k$ ii) $0.2\,k$ iii) $\sqrt{0.017}\,k$
b) i) $\sqrt{2}$ ii) 2

Uniform Circular Motion

1a) An object following a circular path changes direction, and so has a changing (vector) velocity, which in turn creates an acceleration.
b) $F = \frac{mv^2}{r}$, where m = mass, v = linear velocity, r = radius of circle
c) i) $\frac{GMm}{r^2} = \frac{mv^2}{r}$ ii) $v = \sqrt{\left(\frac{GM}{3r_E}\right)} = \sqrt{\left(\frac{gr_E}{3}\right)} = 4.6\,kms^{-1}$

2a) $7.3 \times 10^{-5}\,rad\,s^{-1}$
b) $467\,ms^{-1}$
c) $0.034\,ms^{-2}$
d) Double

3a) Towards the centre of the circle
b) $10690\,N$
c) Friction between the tyres and the road
d) $11\,ms^{-2}$

4a) i) $5.8\,N$ ii) $2.9\,N$ iii) $1.8\,s$ iv) $1.7\,ms^{-1}$
b) If the string is horizontal, there is no vertical component of the tension in the string to balance the object's weight, so the object would accelerate downwards.

Gravitation

1 $-6.3 \times 10^7\,Jkg^{-1}$

2a) $0\,J$
b) $0\,J$
c) $2\,kJ$

3a) $G/4$ to the right
b) $50\,G$

4 $0.225\,m$

Electrostatics

1a) $5.6 \times 10^4\,N$; attractive
b) $6.2 \times 10^3\,N$
c) $9 \times 10^5\,N$

2a) $1.0 \times 10^6\,NC^{-1}$
b) $1.4 \times 10^6\,V$
c) $0.24\,J$

3a) i) $-60\,\mu J$ ii) $0\,J$ iii) $20\,\mu J$
b) Straight lines directed radially outward, perpendicular to the equipotentials

Magnetism

1a) Same direction as other wire
b) $2.7\,A$

2a) X south Y north
b) $1\,T$

3a) RHS moves out of page
b) $2°$

Magnetic Induction

1

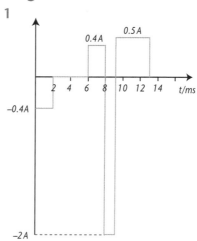

2 $150\,\text{ms}^{-1}$

3a) $1.3\,\text{Wb}$
b) 0
c) $3.1\,\text{V}$

AC Theory

1a) $50\,\text{Hz}$
b) $100\pi\,\text{Hz}$
c) $10\,\text{V}$
d) $8 \times 10^{-4}\,\text{s}$

2a) $3902\,\Omega$
b) $I = 0.013\,\text{A}$
c) $50.3\,\text{Hz}$
d) $0.025\,\text{A}$
e) 3.7

Particle Accelerators

1a) While the particles are travelling through any one tube they are not accelerated, i.e. they drift, as the whole of an individual tube is at a constant potential difference.
b) i) Tube 1 length = $0.01\,\text{m}$, Tube 2 length = $162.5\,\text{m}$, Tube 3 length = $325\,\text{mm}$
ii) No, relativistic effects would increase the mass of the particle dramatically, i.e.

$$m = \frac{m_0}{\sqrt{1 - v^2/c^2}}$$

also the tubes would have to be very long.

iii) number of gaps = $\dfrac{3 \times 10^8}{3.25 \times 10^7} = 9.2$

Therefore 10 gaps are needed which are provided by 11 tubes.

2 $B = 0.33\,\text{T}$

3 $m = 4.7 \times 10^{-30}\,\text{kg}$

Capacitors

1a) $4 \times 10^{-3}\,\text{C}$
b) $0.04\,\text{J}$
c) $40\,\text{s}$
d) $5\,\text{V}$

e) $1 \times 10^{-3}\,\text{C}$

2a) $0.25\,\text{F}$
b) i) $3\,\text{C}$ ii) $18\,\text{J}$

3 $E_1/E = 5$

The Nucleus and Radioactivity

1a) $x = 84$, $y = 4$
b) alpha particle,
c) $1.5 \times 10^9\,\text{s}$

2 $3.9 \times 10^9\,\text{s}^{-1}$

3 Nuclear fusion is the joining of two light nuclei to form heavier, more stable nuclei. Nuclear fission is the splitting of a heavier nucleus into lighter, more stable nuclei.

4 See diagram on page 50. To the right of Fe56 fission/to the left of Fe56 fusion

5a) Uranium-235
b) By bombardment with neutrons
c) Control rods absorb some of the neutrons. This limits the rate of energy production, which can be controlled by varying the depth of the rods within the reactor.

Thermodynamics

1 Above the critical temperature and at low pressures. a) $1333\,\text{cm}^3$ b) isothermal, $1.47 \times 10^5\,\text{Pa}$ c) The gas cools whist held at constant volume (isovolumetric), so the pressure drops from P_C to P_A. d) It is shown by area enclosed by the cycle

2a) i) $\Delta Q = \Delta U + \Delta W^{by}$ where ΔQ is the heat supplied, ΔU the change in internal energy (PE + KE) and ΔW^{by} the work done by the gas on the surroundings.
ii) $80\,\text{MJ}$
iii) No continually operating heat engine can take heat energy from a source and completely transform it into useful work.
iv) Heat needs to be driven from a cold to hot body, as it naturally flows from hot to cold.
b) $130\,\text{W}$

Quantum Duality

1a) Any particle with momentum p has an associated 'de Broglie wavelength' given by:,

$$\lambda = \frac{h}{p} = \frac{h}{mv}$$

where λ is the wavelength, h is Planck's constant and p the particle's momentum.

b) A 'particle' exhibits a dual nature, whereby it can also display wave-like properties. The de Broglie wavelength defines the wavelength of the associated 'particle'.

c) The gain in KE = loss in PE, so

$$\frac{1}{2}mv^2 = qV \Rightarrow v = \sqrt{\frac{2qV}{m}}$$

The de Broglie wavelength is given by

$$\lambda = \frac{h}{p} = \frac{h}{my} = \frac{h}{m\sqrt{2qV/m}} = \frac{h}{\sqrt{2mqV}}$$

d)i) 5.5×10^{-11} m
ii) 6.6×10^{-38} m

2a) Wave–particle duality is the quality of exhibiting both wave and particle properties. What properties are observed depends on the experiment.

b) Young's slits experiment is explained by the light diffracting through the slits and then interfering to create a fringe pattern. Diffraction and interference are wave properties.

c) (see text for details) Apparatus: Monochromatic light (above the threshold frequency) passes through a quartz window and falls on a metal surface in an evacuated chamber. The emitted photoelectron is repelled from the cathode by applying a variable DC voltage to the sample. The current flowing from the cathode to earth is recorded by an electroscope. Measurements: Record the minimum applied voltage required for zero current to flow at a certain frequency. Repeat for a range of recorded frequencies. Analysis: Plot a graph of V against f. A straight line with a positive gradient and negative V-axis intercept proves Einstein's equation.

d) i) 6.4×10^{-34} Js
ii) 2.0 eV (3.2×10^{-19} J).

Astrophysics

1 As diagram in point 6 of 'Improve Your Knowledge'

2i)
$$I = \frac{L}{4\pi d^2} \Rightarrow L = I 4\pi d^2 = 5 \times 10^{-6}$$
$$\times 4 \times \pi \times (20 \times 10^{20})^2 = 2.5 \times 10^{38} \text{W}$$

ii) Using Stefan's Law;

$$L = 4\pi R^2 \sigma T^4 \Rightarrow$$

$$R = \sqrt{\frac{L}{4\pi\sigma T^4}} = \sqrt{\frac{2.5 \times 10^{38}}{4 \times \pi \times 5.67 \times 10^{-8} \times 5200^4}}$$

$$\therefore R = 6.9 \times 10^{14} \text{m}$$

3a)

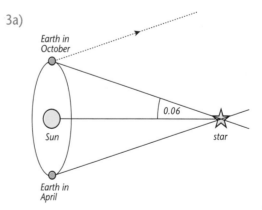

b)
$$d = \frac{1}{0.06} = 16.67 \text{pc}$$

$$1\text{pc} = 3 \times 10^{16} \text{m} \Rightarrow d = 16.67 \times 3 \times 10^{16} = 5 \times 10^{17} \text{m}$$

4a) The Big Bang Theory

b) Red shifts have been observed, indicating an expanding universe.

Cosmic microwave background radiation suggests a universe average temperature of 2.728 K which is very close to that predicted to be the remnant heat of the very hot Big Bang.

The observed abundances of helium, deuterium and lithium are in the ratios predicted by the model.

The temperature of distant galaxies is greater than those closer. This suggests that galaxies are cooling since the information received from distant galaxies originated from further back in time.

5 Main Sequence → Red Giant → mass ≥ 8 solar masses → Supernova → mass ≥ 2.5 solar masses → Black Hole

6 If $\rho < \rho_c$, endless expansion (open or unbounded universe).

If $\rho > \rho_c$, expansion will cease followed by contraction i.e. Big Crunch (closed or bound universe).

If $\rho = \rho_c$, endless expansion at an ever decreasing rate tending to a finite maximum (flat or marginally bounded universe).

ρ_c = critical density.

Medical Physics

1a)

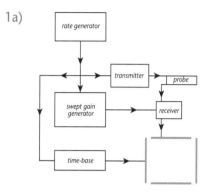

b) $\text{width} = \frac{\text{speed} \times \text{time}}{2} = 1500 \times 0.1 \times 10^{-3}$
$= 7.5 \, \text{cm}$

2a)

ratio of peak heights = $80^2/50^2$

$\dfrac{E_{max\,80}}{E_{max\,50}} = \dfrac{8}{5}$

b) Filtering is the removal of low-energy photons from the X-ray beam. These would otherwise be absorbed by the body and could cause tissue cell damage due to ionisation. The beam has an increased quality following filtering, i.e. it is harder. This is achieved using a few millimetres of aluminium.

c) i)

$$I = I_0 e^{-\mu x} \Rightarrow \ln\left(\frac{I}{I_0}\right) = \mu x$$

$$\therefore \mu = \frac{1}{x}\ln\left(\frac{I_0}{I}\right) = \frac{1}{5 \times 10^{-3}}\ln 5 = 320 \, \text{m}^{-1}$$

ii)

$$x_{\frac{1}{2}} = \frac{\ln 2}{321.9} = 2.2 \text{ mm}$$

3 $\quad \dfrac{1}{T_e} = \dfrac{1}{T_b} + \dfrac{1}{T_r} \Rightarrow \dfrac{1}{T_b} = \dfrac{1}{T_e} - \dfrac{1}{T_r} = \dfrac{1}{1.2} + \dfrac{1}{2}$

$T_b = 0.75$ hours

The half-life is considerably less than for a healthy organ. This suggests that the organ is overactive.

Materials

1a) The resultant force is a combination of the attractive and repulsive electrostatic forces between the particles. The equilibrium separation is when the force is zero.
b) see the *Improve your knowledge*, point 1
c) see the *Improve your knowledge*, point 1 for Hooke's law and thermal expansion.

2a) An edge dislocation is a disruption to the regular stacking sequence in a crystal as an extra plane of atoms has been added or is missing. See *Improve your knowledge*, point 2, for diagram.
b) see *Improve your knowledge*, point 2.

3 Metal fatigue occurs when a metal is subjected to continuous cycles of increasing and decreasing stress. The metal fractures, even though the maximum stress applied may be below the ultimate tensile strength (UTS) of the material. This is important in aircraft or bicycle frame design.

4a) An alloy is a metallic material formed by chemically combining two or more elements. Usually one element forms a lattice and the other acts as an impurity in the structure, by deforming the lattice.
b) see *Improve your knowledge*, point 3.

Synoptic

1a) The magnetic field, B
b) The field (B) always acts at 90° to the direction of motion. Work is only done by a force if the body moves in the direction of the force – which it does not here.
c) Magnetic force = centripetal force;
$Bqv = mv^2/r$, $r = mv/Bq$
d) & (e) see table

d)	Charge (e)	Mass (u)	e) path
Neutron	0	1	(iii)
Proton	+1	1	(i)
α particle	+2	4	(ii)
β particle	-1	1/1800	(iv)
γ radiation	0	0	(iii)

f) no change in motion
g) change speed only, not direction (unless it is simply reversed)

1a)

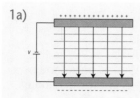

b)i) 444 Vm⁻¹; 2.0 ×10¹³Vm⁻¹;
ii) 67V; 6.0 × 10¹¹V;   iii) 888N; 4 × 10¹³N

b)i) $444\,\text{Vm}^{-1}$; $2.0 \times 10^{13}\,\text{Vm}^{-1}$;
ii) $67\,\text{V}$; $6.0 \times 10^{11}\,\text{V}$;   iii) $888\,\text{N}$; $4 \times 10^{13}\,\text{N}$

c) X: constant acceleration towards the negative plate; Y: repelled from +Q with an acceleration that decreases as $1/r^2$.

2a) $2.1 \times 10^6\,\text{ms}^{-1}$

b) $1.5 \times 10^{-5}\,\text{m}$

3a) $72\,\mu\text{C}$

b) $432\,\mu\text{J}$

c) $66\,\mu\text{C}$

4a)i) $1.97\,\text{Nm}^{-1}$ ii) $1\,\text{m}$
b) Spring system: no change, as mass and spring constant are the same everywhere in the universe.
Pendulum: no oscillations, $g = 0$ so oscillations would have an infinite period.

5a)

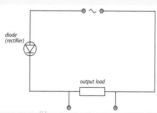

b)

c) By connecting a capacitor in parallel with the rectifier output.

d)

6a) The rate at which energy is delivered by the heater is equal to the rate at which the water removes energy from the heater chamber. Therefore, the total heat flow into the system is zero and the system is in a 'steady state' with a constant output water temperature.
b) $6.7 \times 10^7\,\text{J}$
c) $6.0 \times 10^{-5}\,\text{m}^3\text{s}^{-1}$

Notes

Notes